Encyclopedia of Animals

A Complete Guide to Animals

CONTENTS

RAINFOREST CREATURES

SAFARI CREATURES

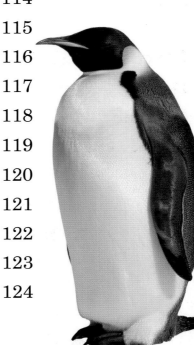

LIFE ON THE MOUNTAINS

Mountains make up about a fifth of the Earth. They give us about 80 per cent of the world's fresh water and support an amazing number of animals, birds and plants.

🐾 *Life on the mountains is not easy because of the harsh climate, strong winds, snowstorms and slippery ice*

Too cold to bear!

It can be extremely cold up in the mountains. Even in summers, temperatures do not rise above 15° Celsius (59° Fahrenheit) in many mountain regions. In winters, for as long as six to eight months, temperatures can fall below freezing. Since the air is so thin, plants and trees do not grow beyond a point. However, some animals and birds are capable of living even above the tree line. These creatures have developed special characteristics to fight the harsh conditions.

Woolly protection

Most mountain animals have a thick, furry coat that keeps them warm through winter. For some, this coat is thinner in summer. Even the feet are protected by fur. These animals are usually warm-blooded, although certain insects are also found here. However, reptiles cannot survive the harsh weather as they would freeze. Some mountain creatures also have small ears and short legs that reduce heat loss.

🐾 *Bighorn sheep have a thick coat to protect them in freezing temperatures*

Walking on ice

It is not easy to walk on snow or ice. If the snow is deep, feet sink in, while one can slip and fall on ice. So how do mountain creatures move about in winter? Most animals that live on mountains have a leathery pad on the bottom of their feet. This pad helps them get a good grip on the ice. The paws of animals like the snow leopard and cougar are large. This distributes their weight and prevents them from sinking into the snow.

Other adaptations

The higher one climbs a mountain, the more difficult it is to breathe. This is because there is very little air at high altitudes. How do mountain creatures breathe in such conditions? All mountain creatures have large and powerful lungs, and more haemoglobin in their blood. These special features help the mountain animals to breathe easily even at higher altitudes. Some sleep through the winter. Bears are known to sleep all through the winter in caves or under the ground. Animals that hibernate eat a lot just before winter. They then retreat into warm burrows or caves and sleep until spring. Some animals, especially birds, migrate to warmer regions.

🐾 Paws of a snow leopard

🐾 The pika is one of the mountain creatures that does not hibernate and is active throughout the freezing winter

COUGAR

The cougar is also known as puma, catamount and mountain lion. It is found in North, Central and South America. It is the largest wild cat in North America after the jaguar.

Cougar watch

Cougars live in rainforests, prairies, deserts and mountains. Depending on their habitat, cougars have a sandy brown to reddish brown coat. Cougars that live on mountains have a thicker coat. The fur is short and has no markings. The cougar has a small head, short, rounded ears and muscular legs. The hind legs are longer than the front legs.

Skilled hunter

Cougars are excellent hunters. They stalk their prey for a while, and then pounce on it. A cougar can leap about 12m (40 feet), and jump vertically about 5m (16 feet). Once the cougar has caught its prey, it kills the victim by biting its neck, using sharp teeth. After eating, cougars bury the remains of their prey, saving it for another meal.

The mighty cougar

Young cougars

A female cougar gives birth to 2-4 cubs.
Cougar cubs are born with spots that
disappear completely by 15 months.
They remain with their mother for about
two years. When they are old enough,
the cubs leave their mother to mark
their own territory. The cubs of a litter
usually stay together until they are
confident enough to settle in their
own home ranges.

Living alone

Cougars are not fond of company. They
prefer to live alone and are protective
about their territory. A male cougar's
home range rarely overlaps that of
another male. However, males can share
small parts of their home range with
females. Territories are marked with
scratches on logs, claw marks on
the dirt or snow and with urine.

🐾 *A cougar poised to pounce*

🐾 *A cougar scratching on a log
of wood to mark its territory*

CREATURE PROFILE

Common name: Cougar

Scientific name: *Felis concolor*

Found in: North, Central and
South America

Size: Adult males: 68-104 kg
(150-230 pounds)

Adult females: 35-60 kg
(77-132 pounds)

Prey: Deer, elk, beavers,
porcupines, raccoons and
squirrels

Enemies: Humans. Cougars
are often killed out of fear
or to protect cattle

Status: Threatened. There are
less than 50,000 cougars left

SNOW LEOPARD

The snow leopard can be found in the mountain ranges of central Asia. It is well-adapted to its cold habitat. It has thick, whitish-grey fur with spots, a long furry tail and huge, furry paws.

Leopard

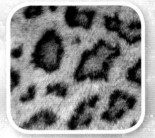
Snow leopard

Jaguar

Life in the mountains

The snow leopard has many features that enable it to live comfortably in the mountains. The cat's unique colour provides good camouflage on bare rocks as well as snow-covered slopes. The snow leopard also has large nostrils, wide chest and short forelimbs. Its woolly undercoat protects it from the cold. The bottoms of the paws are covered with fur to keep the snow leopard's feet warm and prevent it from sinking into the snow.

Not a leopard

The snow leopard is not a true leopard. This wild cat cannot roar like any of the big cats including the leopard. Moreover, the snow leopard crouches over its food while eating, just like domestic cats do. The spots on the snow leopard's fur are also different from those of the leopard. In fact, the snow leopard has dark grey rosettes with spots inside, like the jaguar. Its head and face is covered with smaller black spots.

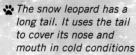
🐾 *The snow leopard has a long tail. It uses the tail to cover its nose and mouth in cold conditions*

Prey and hunting

Like all cats, the snow leopard is also a good, powerful hunter. It can capture prey more than double its size. It is known to eat any animal it can find, from large mammals like ibex and wild boars to small birds and rodents. The snow leopard usually stalks its prey and pounces on it from distances as far as 15m (50 feet).

Who's afraid of heights?

The snow leopard likes to lead a solitary life. This is probably why it lives high up in the mountains. During summers, the snow leopard climbs up to a height of about 6,000m (19,685 feet) — even trees do not grow at these heights! In winters, however, the large cat comes down to the forests at an altitude of about 2,000m (6,562 feet).

🐾 The snow leopard is a large cat adapted to moving about in snowy mountain ranges

🐾 The eyes of snow leopards have round pupils unlike domestic and other small cats

CREATURE PROFILE

Common name: Snow leopard

Scientific name: *Uncia uncia*

Found in: The Himalayas, Altai and Hindu Kush mountains in central Asia

Length: Adult males:
1.8-2.1m (6-7 feet)

Adult females:
1.5-1.7m (5-5.5 feet)

Prey: Ibex, wild boars, deer, hare, tahr, marmots and small birds

Enemies: Humans. Snow leopards are hunted for their beautiful fur and also their bones, which are used to make traditional medicines in Asia

Status: Endangered. There are only about 7,300 snow leopards left in the world

LYNX

The lynx is a medium-sized wild cat that is found mainly in mountainous regions. It has a short tail, a tuft of hair on the tip of the ears, and large, padded paws fit for a life on snow. It inhabits dense forests on mountains and rarely ventures above the tree line.

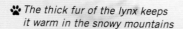

🐾 *The thick fur of the lynx keeps it warm in the snowy mountains*

Three of a kind

There are three varieties of lynx in the world— the Eurasian, the Iberian and the Canadian. The Eurasian lynx is found throughout Europe and Siberia, while the Iberian lynx is limited to parts of Spain. Both species have thick, spotted fur, long whiskers and large feet. However, the Eurasian lynx is larger than its Iberian cousin. The Canadian lynx, found in Canada and Alaska, is closer in size to the Iberian Lynx.

🐾 *The greyish brown coat of the lynx is occasionally marked with dark brown spots*

Hunting skills

The Iberian lynx prefers to hunt through the night, while the Eurasian lynx is active early in the morning or late afternoon. Both species feed on rabbits, deer, small birds and foxes. The lynx usually waits patiently for its prey to come close before pouncing on it. However, the lynx is also known to chase its prey over short distances.

Living the lynx way

Lynx lead solitary and secretive lives, coming together only during the breeding season. The lynx spends most of its time on the ground, although it can climb trees when necessary. The cat uses its extraordinary sense of hearing and sight to track down prey. Females take their cubs out on hunting trips to teach them how to hunt.

🐾 *The solitary and elusive lynx*

🐾 *The lynx has sharp pointed teeth for cutting and slicing the flesh of its prey. It has a bristly tongue that helps to scrape the meat off the bones*

CREATURE PROFILE

Common name: Eurasian lynx, Iberian lynx. Canadian lynx

Scientific name: *Lynx lynx, Lynx pardinus, Lynx canadensis*

Found in: Europe and Siberia (Eurasian lynx), Spain (Iberian lynx), Canada and Alaska (Canadian Lynx)

Size: Eurasian lynx: 18-21 kg (40-44 pounds). A few rare animals weigh 38 kg (83 pounds)

Iberian lynx: about 12.8-26.8 kg (28-69 pounds)

Canadian lynx: 7-14 kg (15-31 pounds)

Feed on: Rabbits, deer, hare, small birds, squirrels and foxes

Enemies: Humans. All three species have been hunted for their thick beautiful fur

Status: Iberian lynx — Endangered

MOUNTAIN RODENTS

Rodents make up the largest group of mammals. Some common rodent species are rats, mice, squirrels, hamsters and guinea pigs. Most rodents live in forests and in the open plains. Some live in the mountains. They have special features that help them survive the very cold climate.

Marmot

Marmots are large ground squirrels that live in North America and Europe. Marmots live in burrows and are social animals. A marmot colony can have 50 members. Sometimes, one member sits outside the burrow and keeps guard. When the guard spots danger, it warns the colony with a high-pitched whistle. Marmots are extremely territorial and defend their colony and children fiercely. Marmots mark territory by smearing rocks with a substance secreted from their chest glands.

❀ The marmot has a soft, thick fur, which keeps it warm

❀ The marmot lives in burrows and hibernates throughout the winter

Alpine Chipmunk

Alpine chipmunks are found in the Sierra Nevada Mountains in California. They live at altitudes of 2,300-3,900m (7,546-12,795 feet). Alpine chipmunks are the smallest in the chipmunk family. They are yellowish-grey and have light contrasting stripes. Alpine chipmunks mainly live on the ground, but can climb trees when in danger. Like all mountain rodents, alpine chipmunks also hibernate during winter. They eat a lot through summer, storing huge amounts of fat that come in useful during hibernation. Food is also stored away in burrows, so that the animals can eat whenever they wake up during winter.

🐾 *The alpine chipmunk has stripes on its face, unlike ground squirrels*

Chinchilla

Chinchillas are mountain rodents seen mostly at night. These furry animals are found on the Andes mountains in South America. Chinchilla is considered to have the softest fur in the world, which they are hunted for. The fur of these rodents is so dense that parasites like fleas cannot live in it, as they would suffocate. Chinchillas can often be seen bathing in volcanic ash or dust to remove oil and moisture from their fur. They live in burrows or rock crevices and are agile, able to jump up to five feet high.

🐾 *The soft-coated chinchilla lives in burrows or crevices in rocks*

CREATURE PROFILE

Common name: Chinchilla

Scientific name: *Chinchilla brevicaudata*

Found in: Andes Mountains in South America

Weight: 453-680 g (1-1.5 pounds)

Feed on: Grass, herbs and other mountain vegetation

Enemies: Humans. Chinchillas have been hunted almost to extinction for their valuable fur

Status: Critically endangered

GIANT PANDA

The giant panda is well known for its unique black and white colouring. This member of the bear family lives in mountainous regions in south central China and is highly revered in the country. The panda is an omnivore, however, most of its diet consists of bamboo shoots and leaves.

Panda features

The giant panda has a bulky body like all bears. Its coat is mainly white with black legs, ears, shoulders and black patches around the eyes. The panda has an enlarged wrist bone that acts as a thumb and helps it grasp things like the bamboo. Pandas usually live on the ground but are excellent climbers. When in danger they can also swim.

❧ The panda eats sitting in an upright position, using its front paws to hold the food

Living alone

Giant pandas are shy creatures and prefer to live alone. Males are not territorial and move in larger areas than females, which defend their turf. Pandas are active both during the day and at night. They are also very vocal and use different sounds to communicate.

Endangered pandas

Giant pandas are the most endangered bear species. Their main food source is bamboo. The destruction of bamboo forests has, therefore, caused a drastic fall in the panda population. Pandas were previously targeted by poachers for their luxurious fur. Wearing panda fur was once considered a sign of courage in China. Panda skin was also in demand in Hong Kong, Japan and many eastern countries.

🐾 The panda has a very thick, oily and woolly fur that keeps it warm in its cold and wet mountain habitat

🐾 The panda has five clawed fingers and an unusual wrist bone. The short claws help it to grab onto tree barks

BLACK BEAR

Black bears are shy, so they live in places that are difficult to reach or have thick vegetation. These animals are usually found in steep mountains and thick forests.

The black bear is an exceptional tree climber

The American black bear

Bear facts

There are two kinds of black bears — the American and the Asiatic. Both species have a large, stocky body covered with shaggy, black or dark brown hair. They have small eyes, rounded ears, a long snout and a short tail. The Asiatic black bear has a cream v-shaped mark on the chest, and a small white crescent on the throat.

Good climbers

The black bear's hind legs are slightly longer than the front legs. The paws have sharp, non-retractable claws. The five claws on each paw help them climb, tear and dig. If ever you come face to face with a black bear, do not climb a tree, it will not help! Black bears are skilful and graceful climbers. They use their sharp claws to get a good grip on the tree trunk and climb quite fast. Black bears usually climb trees when faced with some threat. Mother bears send their cubs up a tree at the sign of potential danger.

Sleeping through winters

Like most bear species, black bears hibernate. Animals hibernate to avoid the effect of winter. They eat voraciously just before the onset of winter so that they can store the necessary fat. Some black bears sleep right through the winter, while some sleep only during the coldest period. The hibernation period usually depends on the availability of food.

🐾 The Asiatic black bear has a cream 'v' on its chest and has larger ears than its American cousin

Waste to wealth

During hibernation, the bears do not excrete waste. Instead, they convert the waste material into valuable proteins. The heartbeat of the animal also drops during this time. However, the body temperature does not reduce much because of their highly insulative fur. Therefore, black bears can wake up from their winter sleep any time.

CREATURE PROFILE

Common name: Asiatic black bear; American black bear

Scientific name: *Ursus thibetanus; Ursus americanus*

Other name: American black bears are also sometimes called cinnamon bears

Found in: The Himalayas, Vietnam, China and Thailand; North America,

Length: Asiatic black bear: 1.2-1.8m (4-6 feet)

American black bear: 1.2-2m (4-6.5 feet)

Feed on: Grass, fruit, berries, roots, insects and carrion

Enemies: Tigers, wolves and mountain lions feed on cubs and wounded black bears. Humans kill them for sport, meat and body parts

Status: Vulnerable

SNOW MONKEY

The snow monkey, also known as Japanese macaque, is the only monkey to be found in snowy regions. This species is found throughout Japan, especially in the north. It has greyish brown fur, red face and bottom, and a short tail.

Surviving the cold

The snow monkey lives in a variety of habitats, including places with freezing winters. It easily survives temperatures as low as -15° C (50° F). This is because it has a thick, furry coat that grows thicker during winters. Snow monkeys also spend a lot of time in hot springs to keep themselves warm.

Eating healthy

The snow monkey's diet changes with the seasons. It eats fruits and berries, seeds, leaves, roots, bird's eggs and insects. In summer, snow monkeys eat leaves and flowers, and in winters they feed on tree bark. The snow monkey is quite finicky. It always washes its food before eating.

🐾 A female snow monkey basking in the sun

🐾 A snow monkey using its hands to eat

A happy family

Snow monkeys live in troops consisting of 20-30 members. Sometimes the troop can have as many as 100 individuals. The size of the troop depends on the availability of food. These troops are made of a few adult males and more than double their number of females. The females normally spend their whole life in the same group, taking care of one another and the young ones. The males leave the group before reaching adulthood. They join and leave several groups.

Living in harmony

Snow monkeys are extremely social and enjoy playing and grooming one another. These peace-loving creatures help one another in caring and protecting the young.

🐾 *Snow monkeys keeping themselves warm by hugging one another*

CREATURE PROFILE

Common name: Snow monkey, Japanese macaque

Scientific name: *Macaca fuscata*

Found in: Mountains and highlands of Japan

Weight: Adult male: 10-14 kg (22-30 pounds)

Adult female: about 6 kg (13 pounds)

Feed on: Seeds, roots, fruit, berries, leaves, insects and bark

Enemies: Humans. Snow monkeys are considered pests and killed in great numbers by farmers. Deforestation has drastically reduced their natural habitat

Status: Threatened. The population of snow monkeys is declining drastically

MOUNTAIN GORILLA

Mountain gorillas are found predominantly in the Virunga volcanic mountains in central Africa. They are the largest of all primates.

Life in the mountains

Mountain gorillas have dark, silky coats, stocky bodies, long, muscular arms, large heads and powerful jaws. Males are much larger than females and have sharp canine teeth. Adult males are called silverbacks as they develop a large patch of greyish silver hair on their backs when they mature. Their long hair helps mountain gorillas to combat the cold climate of the mountains.

Time for a nap! A gorilla sleeping on soft grass

Walk like a gorilla

Mountain gorillas have extremely long and muscular arms, and shorter legs. These creatures usually walk on all fours. They keep their feet flat on the ground, and use their powerful arms to swing the body forward. The weight of the whole body is supported by the knuckles that are placed on the ground in front of the animal.

The mountain gorilla's knuckles are specially adapted to take the weight of the whole body

All in the family

Like all apes, mountain gorillas are a highly social species. They live in groups consisting of one dominant male and a harem of females and their young. The young gorillas are taken care of by the females. Mountain gorillas are usually not territorial, but the leader can get aggressive if he feels threatened. The members of a group travel together.

Good communicators

Mountain gorillas communicate with one another using a variety of sounds. These include grunts, growls, chuckles and hoots. They also use facial expressions and gestures like beating their chest to communicate a wide range of emotions.

🐾 *Grooming is an important part of a gorilla's social life. Female gorillas groom one another, the young ones and silverbacks*

CREATURE PROFILE

Common name: Mountain gorilla

Scientific name: *Gorilla gorilla beringei*

Found in: Virunga volcanic range between Zaire, Rwanda and Uganda

Size: Adult male: 204-227 kg (450-500 pounds)

Adult female: 68-113 kg (150-250 pounds)

Feed on: Roots, leaves, stems, shrubs, bamboo shoot, flowers, fruit, fungi and insects

Enemies: Humans. Mountain gorilla habitats are being destroyed to make way for agricultural land

Status: Critically endangered. There are hardly 400 mountain gorillas left in the wild

RED DEER

The red deer, known as elk or wapiti in North America, is the second largest of all deer species in the world after the moose. This animal prefers mountains and open meadows and avoids dense forests. During summers, the red deer moves up to higher altitudes.

Fit for the mountains

Red deer range in colour from dark brown during winter, to tan in summer. These animals have a characteristic light-coloured rump. Males have a shaggy mane that covers the neck. Red deer have heavy winter coats that are shed just before summer. They have a long head, large ears, short tail and long legs. Males have beautiful antlers branching out of the top of their heads.

Fighting for a mate

The red deer's mating ritual is called a rut. An adult male chooses a harem of females. Sometimes two or more males show interest in a harem, and they fight to decide the winner. Stags often bellow to scare the rival away. They also assess each other's body and antler size, with the smaller opponent often backing down. If neither stag backs down, it leads to a clash of the antlers.

CREATURE PROFILE

Common name: Red deer

Scientific name: *Cervus elaphus*

Found in: Europe, and parts of Asia and North America

Height: Adult male: about 1.6m (5.2 feet) at the shoulder

Adult female: 1.4m (4.5 feet) at the shoulder

Feed on: Grass, leaves and woody growth like cedar, wintergreen and red maple

Enemies: Mountain lions, wolves, bears and humans

Status: Excessive hunting for their skin and antlers has resulted in a drastic decline in the red deer population over the years

Family life

A herd can consist of as many as 400 individuals. The male and female herds come together during the mating season and stay together through winter. In summer, the herds separate. The females leave to give birth. Females with calves often form separate nursery herds and take care of their calves.

❧ *Male red deer using their antlers to fight each other in the mating season*

LLAMA AND ALPACA

Llamas and alpacas belong to the same family as camels. Both animals are found in South America and neither exists in the wild. Llamas were originally found in North America. They migrated to South America and became the main mode of transportation for the Incas.

🐾 *The soft white fleece of the alpacas can be dyed in any colour*

Unique features
Unlike a camel, a llama does not have a hump. Like camels, llamas have a long neck, rounded muzzle, a cleft in the upper lip and long, slender legs. The hoof pads are thick and leathery and help llamas get a grip on the rocky surface. Their long furry coats vary from white to reddish brown to black. They also have a lot of haemoglobin in their blood. This helps llamas survive at high altitudes, where there is little oxygen.

Beware, the llama!
Llamas prefer to live in herds of about 20. A male leads the herd and defends it fiercely. Males often fight for dominance, biting legs and wrapping their necks around one another. The male that is pushed to the ground is the loser. When threatened, llamas charge, spit, bite and kick the enemy. However, llamas are friendly creatures and make good pets.

Defending territory
Llamas are territorial even in captivity. However, if animals like sheep are kept in the same area, llamas adopt them and defend them. This makes llamas good guard animals for sheep, goats, horses and other domesticated animals.

Alpaca
Alpacas look like large sheep with a long necks. Alpacas are smaller than llamas. They live in herds and are gentle and friendly. However, they can be aggressive when threatened. Alpacas have been domesticated for thousands of years. However, unlike llamas, alpacas are not used as beasts of burden. They are bred for wool and meat. The fleece of alpacas is luxurious. It yields much softer and lighter wool than the wool obtained from sheep.

CREATURE PROFILE

Common name: Llama

Scientific name: *Lama glama*

Found in: South America, near south-east Peru and western Bolivia and Chile

Height: 1.2m (3.9 feet) at the shoulder

Weight: 136-204 kg (300-450 pounds)

Feed on: Shrubs, grass, leaves, lichen

Enemies: Mountain lions, cougars, dogs, humans

Status: Domestication has helped to revive their population

🐾 *A llama and its young one*

PIKA

The pika is a small animal that belongs to the rabbit and hare family. It is sometimes known as rock rabbits or coney. There are about thirty different species of pikas, which look a lot like hamsters, even though they are more closely related to rabbits.

Life in the mountains

Pikas are found in cold climates. They are widely distributed throughout Asia, North America and parts of eastern Europe. Pikas usually form huge colonies. Members of a colony gather food together and look after one another. However, some species prefer to lead a solitary life. In Europe and Asia, pikas have been known to share their burrows with snowfinches that nest with them.

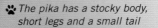

The pika has a stocky body, short legs and a small tail

Preparing for winter

Pikas are most active before winter. These creatures do not hibernate. Instead, they are active throughout. Some species spend the day basking in the sun, and crouching on rocks. Most pikas collect fresh grass and lay them out to dry. They then store this dry grass in their burrows. The dry grass serves as warm bedding as well as food for the animal during the harsh winter. Only the Royle's pika does not make grass piles.

Family life

Pikas that live in colonies make burrows. These are very complicated and have many tunnels and entrances. This not only allows the pika to forage across a wider area, but also helps it to retreat quickly to safety in case of danger. Pikas find more food on the plateau meadowlands. Families are highly territorial, and males chase members of other families away, especially when they are busy drying grass and stacking hay.

The pika bask in the sun on rocks matching the colour of their coat

ROCKY MOUNTAIN GOAT

The rocky mountain goat is a native of North America. Even though it resembles the common goat, the rocky mountain goat actually belongs to the antelope family. The main habitats of this species are the steep, rocky cliffs of alpine and sub-alpine areas.

🐾 The calf learns to jump and climb when it is just a few minutes old!

Physical features

Rocky mountain goats have stout bodies, which is covered with thick fur. The colour of the fur varies from white to yellowish. Since they live in regions where there is winter for as long as nine months, they have a coat that is well adapted to bearing the freezing temperatures. They have a dense, woolly undercoat and long hair, about 20 cm (8 inches) in length, in the outer layer. This thick coat protects the goats from the cold and harsh mountain climate by keeping them cosy and warm. In summer, when the temperature rises, mountain goats rub themselves against trees or rocks to shed their woolly coats. Both male and female goats have prominent beards, short tails and long black horns.

Living in herds

Rocky mountain goats form large herds during winter and spring. In summer, these animals form smaller groups or even live alone. They are most active from dawn to dusk. Adult females lead a herd most of the time except during the breeding season. That is when males take over and participate in dominance fights to win over the females. Unlike other antelopes, mountain goats do not go in for head-to-head fights.

Warring nannies

Female rocky mountain goats or nannies also take part in dominance fights. For most of the year, a dominant female leads the herd. These creatures are protective and often become violent while defending their herd and territory. A fight between two nannies usually ends up involving the rest of the females in the herd too. Fights may sometimes lead to the death of one of the rivals. Weaker opponents usually give up by lying on the ground.

🐾 The rocky mountain goat is a very good climber

CREATURE PROFILE

Common name: Rocky mountain goat

Scientific name: *Oreamnos americanus*

Found in: Parts of North America

Height: 0.8-1.0m (31-39 inches)

Weight: 45.3-136 kg (100-300 pounds)

Feed on: Grass, lichens, mosses, woody plants and other mountain vegetation

Enemies: Mountain lions and humans. Golden eagles prey on the young

Status: Vulnerable. Mountain goats are killed extensively for their woolly coats and meat

BIGHORN SHEEP

Adult male bighorn sheep have such large, curved horns, no other name would have suited them! Females have shorter, less curved horns. The horns of the male and female bighorn sheep are well suited for their varying behaviour.

Features of the bighorn

Bighorn sheep have a muscular body covered with smooth fur. The coat is similar to a deer's. The outer coat has glossy, brittle guard hairs over a short grey fleece. It is usually a glossy, rich brown in summer, but fades as winter nears. Bighorn sheep have a narrow and pointed muzzle, short, pointed ears and a very short tail. These animals have hard, double-layered skulls designed for combat. A broad tendon that links the skull to the spine helps the head to recoil from hard blows.

Locking horns

Male bighorn sheep are not territorial. However, they fight head-to-head for the attention of a female. Males charge at each other with their heads lowered. A male smashes into his opponent at about 32 kph (20 mph). The ram with the bigger horn holds an advantage. Fights often last as long as 25 hours, with five clashes per hour!

Built for the heights

Bighorn sheep can go up and down cliffs with ease. They usually use small ledges as footholds. Bighorn sheep can leap across distances of about 6m (20 feet). Their hooves are hard outside and softer inside. This helps them climb easily at a speed of up to 24 km/hour (15 mph). On level ground, they can reach speeds of 48 km/hour (30 mph).

Social animals

Bighorn sheep are found on the slopes of the Rocky Mountains in North America. They live in regions with light snowfall, since they cannot dig through deep snow for food. Bighorn sheep are excellent swimmers. They live in herds of 8-10 individuals but sometimes, a herd can have up to 100 members. Males form bachelor herds. If a wolf threatens them, the herd huddles in a circle to face the enemy.

🐾 Bighorn sheep have been hunted so extensively that they are a threatened species

🐾 By the age of 7-8, the bighorn ram can have a set of horns with a full curl and a spread of about 83 cm (33 inches)

CREATURE PROFILE

Common name: Bighorn sheep

Scientific name: *Ovis canadensis*

Found in: North America, especially the Rocky Mountains

Weight: Adult male: 120-130 kg
(264-286 pounds)

Adult female: 53-90 kg
(117-198 pounds)

Feed on: Grass and herbs

Enemies: Mountain lion, coyote, wolf, bear, lynx and human

Status: Threatened. Bighorn sheep populations have been falling due to poaching, diseases from livestock and habitat destruction

IBEX AND TAHR

The ibex and tahr are types of mountain goats. The ibex is found in Eurasia and north Africa. Alpine ibex are usually found at altitudes of over 3,000m (10,400 feet). The tahr is found in parts of Asia.

Alpine Ibex

Alpine ibex have brownish grey coats that become dark brown during winters. Male ibex are usually twice the size of females, and can also be distinguished by their thick, prominent beards. Both males and females have long horns that curve backwards. In some males, the horns can be as long as 1m (3.2 feet). The ibex uses its horn to fight off predators such as lynx, bears, wolves and foxes.

Himalayan Tahr

The Himalayan tahr is one of the three species of tahr. It is found in mountain slopes at altitudes of 3500-5000m (11,482-16,404 ft). The Himalayan tahr is well-suited to life in the mountains. Its hooves have a flexible, rubbery sole that allows the tahr to grip slippery rocks. The tahr is one of the best mountain climbers in the animal world.

Arabian Tahr

The Arabian tahr is found in the Hajar mountains of U.A.E. and the Sultanate of Oman. It is the smallest of the three tahr species but very strong and extremely agile. It is capable of climbing nearly vertical cliffs. Unlike its cousins, this tahr is not found in large herds. It is also very territorial. This species is endangered because of hunting and habitat destruction.

Nilgiri Tahr

The Nilgiri tahr is a goat-like animal with a short coat and short, curved horns. However, unlike the Himalayan tahr, the Nilgiri tahr is more closely related to sheep. Male Nilgiri tahrs are black with a silver saddle and short bristles. Females have greyish brown coats with white bellies. In all three tahr species, the males compete with each other for the attention of the females.

CREATURE PROFILE

Common name: Himalayan tahr

Scientific name: *Hemitragus jemlahicus*

Found in: The Himalayan mountain range

Weight: Adult male: 90-100 kg (198-220 pounds)

Adult female: 60-70 kg (132-154 pounds)

Feed on: Alpine herbs, shrubs and other mountain vegetation

Enemies: Snow leopards and humans

Status: Vulnerable. Over hunting and habitat loss has led to a sharp decline in the population of Himalayan tahrs

❧ *The ibex was once hunted extensively and is now threatened with extinction*

❧ *A Nilgiri tahr has a hard rimmed foot that helps it to climb mountains*

ANDEAN CONDOR

The Andean condor is the largest flying land bird in the western hemisphere. It lives in the Andes Mountains and belongs to the family of New World vultures that evolved from cranes and storks. Andean condors feed on dead animals.

The condor covers a large area while looking for food

Condor facts

Adult Andean condors are mainly black with a frill of white feathers at the base of the neck. When it flies to high altitudes, the condor tucks its head into this frill of feathers to keep the head warm. It also has a band of white feathers on its wings, which have a span of about 3m (10 feet). The neck and head are almost bald. Male condors have a comb on their heads and a wattle near the neck. The skin of the head and neck can turn bright red to warn others. The feet have a long middle toe and the claws are straight and blunt, which helps them to walk.

Condor in flight

The condor is a graceful bird. It can soar to great heights with minimal effort by using natural thermal air streams for elevation. Condors spend a great deal of time looking for food and fly miles to find something to eat.

Clean condors

Condors spend a lot of time grooming and sunning. Condors can be seen basking in the sun with their wings stretched out and turned towards the sun. They preen their feathers and arrange them neatly every day. They also clean their heads and necks after every meal. This is important as condors feed on dead animals, and the decaying flesh can infect them.

National symbol

The Andean condor is the national symbol of Columbia, Ecuador, Peru, Argentina and Chile, such is its status.

Condor parents

Condors nest on rocky ledges at heights of 3,000-5,000m (10,000-16,000 feet). The nest is made of a few sticks or twigs. The female condor lays one or two eggs at a time. The egg hatches in about 58 days. Both parents look after the nestling. The chick grows feathers after six or seven months. The young bird can fly only after it is half a year old and stays with its parents for almost two years.

A condor preparing to take flight

The large and majestic condor

CREATURE PROFILE

Common name: Andean condor

Scientific name: *Vultur gryphus*

Found in: Andes Mountains in South America

Weight: Adult male: 11-15 kg (24-33 pounds)

Adult female: 7.5-11 kg (16.5-24 pounds)

Feed on: Dead animals like rabbits, goats, cattle, deer, horses and coyotes, eggs

Enemies: Humans

Status: Hunting, habitat loss and chemical poisoning have reduced Andean condor populations

GOLDEN EAGLE

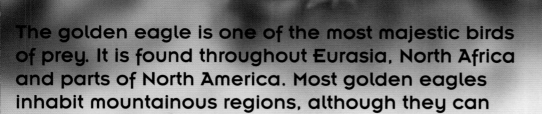

The soaring golden eagle has a wing span of 1.8-2.1m (6-7 feet)

The golden eagle is one of the most majestic birds of prey. It is found throughout Eurasia, North Africa and parts of North America. Most golden eagles inhabit mountainous regions, although they can also be seen in various other habitats.

Physical features

Golden eagles are dark brown, except for a golden patch near the crown, nape and sides of the neck and face. Males and females look similar. The birds have long, broad, brown-grey wings. The tail is grey-brown, while the head, body and smaller feathers on the front of the open wings are almost black. The sharp, curved claws are also black. The feet are yellow. To help retain warmth the legs are feathered down to the toes.

Bonded forever

Golden eagles mate for several years and even for life. The mating pair chase, dive, circle and soar together. They also pretend to attack each other and lock their talons or claws in mid-flight. Nests are made of sticks, grass, leaves, moss, lichen and bark. Both parents incubate the eggs and care for the chicks.

Golden eagle facts

Golden eagles usually stay in one place. Some may migrate short distances for food. Most golden eagles are found in pairs or, otherwise, live alone. Young golden eagles sometimes form small groups. Adults form groups only during harsh winters or when food is abundant. Golden eagles defend their breeding area with aggression.

Hunting together

Golden eagles feed on small mammals like rabbits, hares, marmots and prairie dogs. They also eat smaller birds, reptiles and fish. Sometimes, they kill young deer, coyotes, badgers, cranes and geese. Golden eagles often hunt in pairs. One chases the prey until it gets exhausted, then the other swoops down for the kill.

The mighty golden eagle has dark eyes and excellent vision

CREATURE PROFILE

Common name: Golden eagle

Scientific name: *Aquila chrysaetos*

Found in: Europe, North Asia, Japan, North Africa and North America

Weight: 3.5-6 kg (7.7-13 pounds)

Length: 75-84 cm (29.5-33 inches)

Feed on: Small mammals like rabbits, squirrels, fish, reptiles, and birds Enemies: Wolverines, bears, humans

Status: Vulnerable. Until recently, farmers killed thousands, fearing that the eagles would attack their livestock

OTHER MOUNTAIN BIRDS

The mountains are home to a large variety of birds, including snowfinches, tinamou and chough. Some birds can be found at astonishing altitudes.

Snowfinch

The snowfinch is a type of sparrow found in the mountains of Europe and Asia. It is a large and stocky sparrow about 16.5-19 cm (6-7.5 inches) in length. Most of these birds are found at heights of above 3,500m (11,483 ft). Snowfinches are well adapted to life at such great heights. These birds are so tough that they do not come down to the lowlands even when it is very cold, although they are known to move to slightly lower altitudes in winter. Snowfinches usually make nests in the crevices of rocks, but are also known to take up residence in the burrows of pikas. Their bodies are pale brown on top with white underparts. Their wings have long, white panels that are prominent when the birds are flying. They primarily feed on seeds, insects and worms.

Tinamou

Tinamous are one of the most ancient birds around and include 47 different species. Found mainly in the Andes, they bear a close resemblance to quails, although they are actually related to emus and ostriches. Tinamous have small, rounded bodies, and are able to survive even the harshest winters. They feed on berries and insects and are quite secretive birds. They lay several shiny eggs. The young can run almost as soon as they hatch.

🐾 *The tinamou is protectively covered in greyish brown feathers*

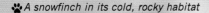

🐾 *A snowfinch in its cold, rocky habitat*

Chough

The chough resembles a crow because of its black plumage. It is found in the mountains of Europe and Asia. It mainly inhabits the highlands. However, in some places these birds live in inland quarries. The two main species of chough are the red-billed and the Alpine chough. The red-billed chough is set apart by its bright red beak. The Alpine chough, on the other hand has a yellow beak. Choughs live in groups. They feed on insects in summer and berries in winter. Choughs are very acrobatic and are known for their graceful flight.

CREATURE PROFILE

Common name: Andean tinamou

Scientific name: *Nothoprocta pentlandii*

Found in: Andean mountains in South America

Length: 25-30 cm (9.8-11.8 inches)

Weight: 800 grams (1.7 pounds)

Feeds on: Seeds, roots, fruit, small reptiles, insects and spiders

Enemies: Humans. Tinamous are killed for their meat

Status: Eleven species are considered threatened, of which two are critically endangered

❧ The Alpine chough has a distinguishing yellow beak

MOUNTAINS IN DANGER

Mountains are some of the most inaccessible places on earth. Despite this, human activities are changing mountain landscapes and endangering ecosystems. As a result some mountain creatures, adapted to the environment and climate there, are dwindling fast. Global warming, deforestation and other unnatural events are affecting the life of mountain creatures, most of which will not survive away from their natural habitat.

🐾 Global warming is melting glaciers.

Climatic changes

Global warming is one of the biggest threats to mountain ecosystems. Increase in overall temperatures has led to more glaciers melting. This means there is less snow cover. Creatures that live on mountains have thick coats that protect them from the cold. Warmer temperatures would make them uncomfortable and ill. Higher temperatures also mean shorter winters. Many mountain creatures sleep through winter. They eat more in summer. If winter days are fewer, these animals will feed longer. This can lead to a shortage of food.

Habitat destruction

Humans are also encroaching upon mountain regions. Forests are often cleared for agriculture. People have also started building more homes on mountains, cutting down trees. Many mountain animals depend on trees to give them protection from the weather and from predators. Deforestation also leads to a higher frequency of landslides and avalanches.

🐾 Large scale deforestation means a shortage of food and habitat for many mountain creatures

Hunting

Many mountain creatures are killed for money. Animals like the snow leopard, chinchillas and giant pandas are killed for their fur. Mountain antelopes are hunted for their coat as well as their antlers. Sometimes, certain animals or birds are killed because they are considered pests. Condors and cougars were hunted as they were mistakenly thought to attack livestock. Hunting has brought many of these creatures close to extinction.

Lack of food

Over hunting of one species often affects the animal that preys on it. Lack of food is one of the major threats facing mountain creatures. When people encroach on mountain regions, their livestock competes with the native animals for food. Many wild animals also catch diseases from animals like cats, dogs and other pets. Wild animals are extremely vulnerable to these diseases since they are not naturally immune to them.

Grazing grounds of mountain creatures infiltrated by domestic cattle

LIFE AT THE POLES

The Arctic Circle marks the start of the most northerly part of the earth and the Antarctic Circle, the most southerly. North of the Arctic Circle and south of the Antarctic Circle are the polar regions. The South Pole is the coldest place on earth. The coldest temperature recorded was -89.4° C (-129° F).

Poles apart

The Polar regions are also the most windy places on earth. Most of the land is covered with ice and snow. Summer comes to the North Pole around June and to the South Pole around December. During summer the polar regions have light 24 hours and no darkness. This is so because the sun never sets. In winter, however, the sun never rises, and there are days when it is dark for 24 hours.

☙ The first expedition to the North pole was made on April 6, 1909 by Robert Edwin Peary, Matthew Henson and four Inuit men

The North Pole

Parts of the Arctic Ocean are frozen throughout the year and the average winter temperature is -30° C (-22° F). Even when the snow melts, the Arctic region is covered with permafrost, a frozen layer of soil just under the surface. Summers are warm enough for some plants to grow. The edge of the Arctic region, covered with short grass, is the tundra. In Finnish, tunturia, from which it gets its name, means, treeless plain.

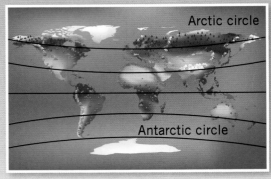

☙ The areas marked in white show the Arctic and the Antarctic circles of the globe

The South Pole

The Antarctic is larger than the United States. It is a frozen, dry and windy continent of glaciers and high mountains. The land is covered with ice about two kilometres thick (1.2 miles). The only people living there are scientists. The vegetation includes 400 types of lichen, 100 species of moss, 30 species of liverwort and around 700 types of algae. The only flowers that grow are hair grass and pearlwort. A few animals such as penguins, whales and seals live here. Squid and ice fish live in the sea. They are food for the albatross, one of the few birds that fly over Antarctica.

Cherish and conserve

Both the North Pole and the South Pole are being affected by pollution. The Great Arctic Reserve, set up by the government of Russia, is one of the largest protected areas in the world. Covering 46,000 sq km (17,760 sq miles), it is a safe home for 700,000 reindeer, polar bears and seals. On the opposite Pole, the Southern Ocean that surrounds Antarctica has been declared an international whale sanctuary.

🐾 *The first humans to reach South pole were Roald Amundsen and his party on December 14, 1911*

FACT FILE

North Pole

Full name: Arctic

Nearest Landmass: Greenland, 724 km (450 miles) south

Water Depth: 4,114m (13,500 feet)

Average Temp.: -18°C (-0.4°F)

Ice Thickness: 0.9-2 metres (3-6 feet)

Earliest explorers: Peary and Henson (1909)

South Pole

Full name: Antarctica

Area: 14,250,000 sq km (5,501,925 sq miles)

Coldest: -89.4°C (-129°F) at Vostok on July 21, 1983

Warmest: -35°C (-31°F)

Wind speed: Up to 320 kph (199 mph)

Earliest explorer: Roald Amundsen (1911)

POLAR BEAR

The polar bear is the largest meat-eating animal on land. It is the only animal that actively hunts humans. It is also the top predator in the Arctic region. It feeds on seals and walruses found in the region. Polar bears are found throughout the Arctic. They usually live on sea ice and along the shores.

🐾 *Polar bears are so well protected that they tend to overheat. They move slowly to avoid overheating. Occasionally they swim to cool down*

🐾 *A Polar bear's nostrils close when it is under water*

Life in the North Pole

The polar bear is large and heavy. It has a small head, long neck, rounded ears and a short tail. The front legs of the polar bear are shorter than the hind legs. The large paws of the bear help spread its weight over a large area. This prevents the ice from breaking under the bear's weight. The bottom of the paws have thick, black pads covered with small bumps, called papillae. The fur and the papillae stop the bear from slipping on ice. Sharp, curved claws are used for extra grip while running or climbing as well as for grasping prey.

Keeping warm

The polar bear is well-adapted for its life in the cold Arctic region. It has a layer of blubber, about 10 cm (4 inches) thick. Blubber is a thick layer of fat found under the skin. It keeps the bear warm both on land and in water. The bear digs a hole in the snow and curls up in it during extremely cold and windy days. It also covers its nose and mouth with its paws on such occasions, so that heat does not escape through these areas. The bear's small ears and short tail also prevents heat loss. Apart from this, the bear has a coat that is about 5 cm (2 inches) thick.

Furry tales

From a distance, the polar bear looks white, even yellowish in colour. The hair that covers the body of the polar bear is, in fact, colourless! The thick coat of the polar bear consists of a dense layer of underhair covered by a thinner layer of clear, hollow guard hair. The inner layer keeps the bear warm, while the guard hair directs sunlight into the inner layer. The outer guard hairs reflect light making the bear appear white.

A watery life

Polar bears are very good swimmers. They have been known to swim continuously for more than 100 km (60 miles) at speeds of about 10 km/hour (6 mph). Polar bears use their front paws as paddles while swimming. The paws are partially webbed for the same reason. The back legs of a polar bear are held flat and used to steer the bear. The layer of blubber keeps the bear warm while swimming. Polar bears are also known to dive, although they do not dive very deep.

🐾 A Polar bear's hair can easily shake off water or ice after a swim

CREATURE PROFILE

Common name: Polar Bear

Scientific name: *Ursus maritimus*

Found in: The Arctic region (Alaska, Canada, Russia, Greenland, Norway)

Length: Adult males: 2.5-3m (8-10 feet)
           Adult females: 2-2.5m (6.5-8 feet)

Prey: Seals (ringed and bearded seals), bird eggs, sea birds, young walruses, dead whales and berries

Enemies: Humans. Polar bears were hunted extensively for their thick fur and meat. Their long canine teeth were used to make jewellery and artefacts

Status: Threatened. Following strict laws, the polar bear population has now become stable. Today, there are about 40,000 polar bears in the Arctic

A BEAR'S LIFE

Polar bears have paw pads with rough surfaces.
These help to prevent them from slipping on the ice.

Going for the kill

The polar bear is one of the best hunters in the bear family. Their favourite prey is ringed seals. They also kill the larger and heavier walrus and beluga whale. They often stand silently by a seal's breathing hole, waiting for it to surface. When the seal comes up for air, the polar bear flips it out with a blow of its large front paw. They sometimes stalk prey or swim beneath the ice looking for food.

What a keen nose!

Polar bears have a keen sense of smell that helps them in hunting. They can detect seal breathing holes covered by layers of ice and snow as far as 1 km (0.62 miles) away. They can see and hear about as well as a human and can swim underwater with their eyes open. An angry polar bear will hiss, snort, growl and roar. Naughty cubs are met with a low growl or a soft cuff from their mother.

Polar bears have 42 teeth which they use for catching food or for aggressive behaviour, and occasionally for displaying affection

Happy birthday, baby bear!

Polar bears are born between the end of November and early January. Most mothers have two cubs at a time while some have one or three. The cubs, born blind, weigh only 0.6 kg (1.32 lb) and are covered with fine hair. They stay inside the den until early April, but do not leave their mother until they are two and- a-half years old. She protects them during this time and teaches them to hunt. They grow very quickly between their first and second birthdays. They feed on their mother's milk, which has more fat in it than the milk of other bears. This helps them fight the cold.

Home, sweet home!

Mother bears prepare a den for their babies at one end of a tunnel. The opening to the tunnel is sealed with soft snow, which traps in air and keeps the den much warmer than outside. Once the cubs are a few months old, the family begins its journey back to the sea so that the mother can hunt for food. On the way, she digs resting pits in the snow to shelter her cubs from the freezing wind where they feed and rest.

🐾 *Polar bears dig a hole in snow and cuddle up to keep themselves warm*

🐾 *Polar bears are extremely protective of their young ones. They risk their own lives in defending their cubs*

ARCTIC SEALS

Seals are sea mammals. Most seals live in or around the Arctic Circle or Antarctica. Seals are pinnipeds or creatures that have flippers instead of limbs. Fur seals are the only seals that have an external ear. Seals are good swimmers, steering with their clawed front flippers and propelling themselves with their rear flippers. They are clumsy on land. Seals live in the coldest places in the world. A layer of blubber keeps them warm. There are six species of Arctic seals.

Harp Seal

Harp seals are born with a yellowish fur. It remains for three days, after which it turns white. This is why they are also called whitecoats. The white colour helps them blend with the snow but the silky, luxurious texture attracts enemies like humans. As the babies grow older, grey patches appear on the white fur. Harp seals get their name from the black horseshoe-shaped patch or harp on the back of adult males. Adult females have a lighter band. Harp seals can dive to 182-275m (600-900 feet) and stay underwater for 15 minutes. Harp seals have a thinner neck than other seals. They swim in large herds of up to 75, diving and leaping.

My! You've grown!

They have a strong sense of smell and the mother can sniff out her own pup from among many others. She nurses it for just two weeks. Her milk, rich in fat, helps the pup grow to about 40 kg (88 lb) with a thick layer of blubber. This is about the time that pups are ready for their first swim. Harp seal pups are among the fastest growing mammals.

❧Harp seal and its pup lying in the snow

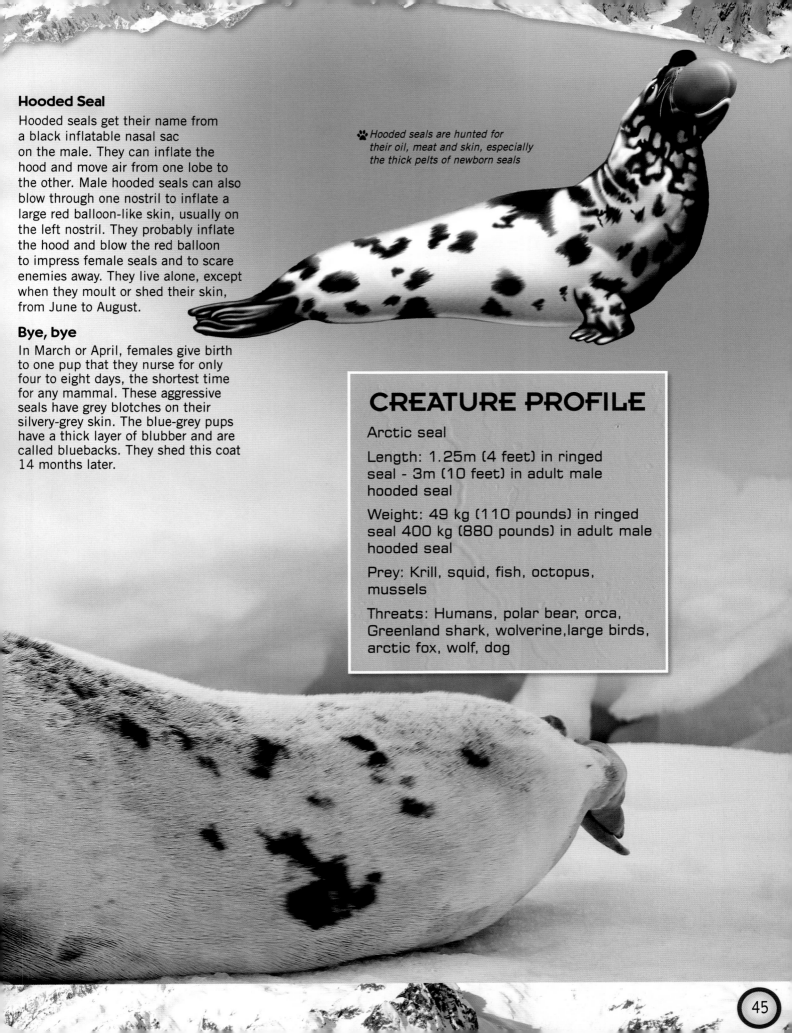

Hooded Seal

Hooded seals get their name from a black inflatable nasal sac on the male. They can inflate the hood and move air from one lobe to the other. Male hooded seals can also blow through one nostril to inflate a large red balloon-like skin, usually on the left nostril. They probably inflate the hood and blow the red balloon to impress female seals and to scare enemies away. They live alone, except when they moult or shed their skin, from June to August.

Bye, bye

In March or April, females give birth to one pup that they nurse for only four to eight days, the shortest time for any mammal. These aggressive seals have grey blotches on their silvery-grey skin. The blue-grey pups have a thick layer of blubber and are called bluebacks. They shed this coat 14 months later.

🐾 *Hooded seals are hunted for their oil, meat and skin, especially the thick pelts of newborn seals*

CREATURE PROFILE

Arctic seal

Length: 1.25m (4 feet) in ringed seal - 3m (10 feet) in adult male hooded seal

Weight: 49 kg (110 pounds) in ringed seal 400 kg (880 pounds) in adult male hooded seal

Prey: Krill, squid, fish, octopus, mussels

Threats: Humans, polar bear, orca, Greenland shark, wolverine, large birds, arctic fox, wolf, dog

SEALS OF ANTARCTICA

There are more seals in the Antarctic than in the Arctic. This is because the Antarctic has more food and fewer enemies for the seal. Seals live throughout the Antarctic region. The southern elephant seal is the largest. The adult males are 4.5m (14-16 feet) long.

🐾 *Crabeater seals moult in January and February. They spend most of their time on the ice when moulting*

Weddell Seal

Named after the British Antarctic explorer James Weddell, these seals live in large groups on the ice. They spend most of their time under water and come up to breathe and to give birth to their pups. Their dark silver-spotted coats have short, dense fur. They use their large canine teeth to scrape holes in the ice and to chew. Their whiskers help them swim around obstacles.

Deep divers

Weddell seals can dive over 609m (2,000 feet) deep. They can stay under the water for an hour and call out loudly to each other under the water. Mother weddell seals give birth to one pup around September. The pups grow from 27 kg (60 pounds) at birth to 90 kg (200 pounds) in eight weeks. By then, they have learnt to swim, hunt and pull themselves out of water onto land. If they see another animal, they roll onto their backs in surrender.

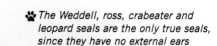

🐾 *The Weddell, ross, crabeater and leopard seals are the only true seals, since they have no external ears*

Crabeater Seal

Crabeater seals have unusual five-point teeth that lock like a strainer to keep the aquatic food in when the water drains out. They eat krill, fish and squid. Their name is the result of a mistake an early scientist made. If another animal comes near, they bare their teeth and snort. Crabeaters can travel for about 56 km (35 miles) on land.

🐾 *Crab eater seals changing their scarred coats*

CREATURE PROFILE

Antarctic seal

Length: Crabeater Seal 2.7-3m (9-10 feet), Weddell seal 3.2m (10.5 feet)

Weight: Crabeater seal about 226 kg (500 pounds), Weddell Seal about 453 kg (1,000 pounds)

Prey: Krill, squid, fish

Threats: Leopard seal, orca

A change of wardrobe

Crabeater seals change their coats with the seasons. A dark grey in winter helps them retain heat. In summer, they turn white. The coat of crabeater seals is prominently scarred. These are scars of the wounds they receive from killer whales and leopard seals. They eat about twice their own weight of krill every month and can eat more krill than any of the baleen or toothless whales. They breed in small groups on the pack ice. Their pups have to grow fast so that they can look after themselves in barely three weeks. Crabeater seals are the most numerous seal species on the Southern ocean.

LEOPARD SEAL

The second largest of the Antarctic seals is the leopard seal. It has a long, slim, torpedo-shaped body. Its name comes from its grey fur spotted with black. It is the only seal that eats other seals. The female leopard seal, usually 3m (9.84 feet) long, is larger than the male!

A keen hunter

This seal has strong jaws, long, sharp teeth and a huge mouth. It also has keen eyesight and can smell under water. It is a powerful swimmer and makes a dangerous enemy for penguins and other seals swimming or resting on the ice. Its head looks more like a reptile's, with nostrils on top of its snout. Its neck and back are strong. Powerful front flippers help steer through the water at speeds of up to 40 km/hour (25 mph). They cannot move as easily on land. Their only enemy is the killer whale.

A varied menu

Their main food is penguins, but they also eat other seals, fish, squid, krill, sea birds and even platypus. They chew with long, pointed, inward-curving teeth. These saw-like teeth come in handy to tear off flesh or to sift out water when they catch krill. They swim fast and far, travelling more than any other seal, sometimes as far as South Africa and Australia.

Since leopard seals do not hunt in open water they do not need to dive for more than fifteen minutes

🐾 *On the surface, Leopard seals appear more squat, while in the ocean they look longer and sleeker like a snake*

Lone mother

Leopard seals live until they are about 26 years old. They live alone, except during the breeding season. A mother has one pup a season, born in a hole that she digs in the ice. The pups are born between November and January. The mother stuffs herself before she leaves the water to give birth, so she can go for several days without eating. The pup is fed on fatty milk, and doubles in size in three months. Three weeks after birth, it is ready for its first swim and goes fishing for krill.

First human prey

Leopard seals seldom attack humans and even swim alongside scientists. But on 22 July 2003, a leopard seal attacked and killed British marine biologist Kirsty Brown, the first recorded human death. With more and more scientists going down to Antarctica, such attacks may increase. There are few threats to these animals, which number about 222,000. Its only enemy is the killer whale. A major threat for the leopard seal would be a drop in the amount of krill, which could happen if the seas of the Antarctic get more polluted.

CREATURE PROFILE

Common name: Leopard seal

Scientific name: *Lydrurga leptonyx*

Found in: The Antarctic region, rarely straying up to South Africa, Australia

Weight: Adult males: 320 kg (705 pounds)
        Adult females: 370 kg (81 pounds)

Length: Adult males: 2.8m (9.1 ft)
        Adult females: 3m (9.8 ft)

Prey: Penguins, other seals, fish, squid, krill, sea birds, platypus

Enemies: Killer whales, humans

WALRUS

The walrus is an Arctic mammal, which has been around for at least 14 million years. It is very large. In fact, it gets its name from the Dutch words, wal (shore) and reus (giant). They can grow up to 4m (14 feet) long, and have long tusks.

Heavier than a polar bear

A male walrus can weigh 800-1,700 kg (1,764-3,748 pounds) but it is the size of the ivory tusks that decides who is the dominant male. Both males and females have tusks. These help them to anchor on the bottom of the ocean (about 95m (304 feet) deep) to dig for clams, snails, shrimps, worms and mussels. A walrus squirts jets of water to bring the clams out and can eat 4,000 clams in one meal. They feed twice a day, eating a quarter of their body weight each time. The tusks, which help them to crack breathing holes in the ice, have age rings. The tusks are used to fend off polar bears and killer whales.

Wowzee whiskers

The walrus has a bristly moustache with about 700 hairs in 13 to 15 rows that help it to feel its way under water. Its thick, armour-like wrinkly skin changes from cinnamon brown or pink to almost white when the walrus is under the chilly water. A 10 cm (3.9 in) layer of blubber or fat keeps them warm. They shed their short hair between June and August. Walruses have 18 teeth, including their tusks, two small eyes and small openings for ears. They have keen sense of hearing. Walruses breathe through their mouth and nostrils, which are just above their whiskers. A walrus swims about 7 km/hour (4.3 mph), but manages short bursts of up to 35 km/hour (21.7 mph).

The longer the tusk of the walrus, the higher is its rank in the group

Family animal

Walruses spend about two-thirds of their time in water and the rest on ice floes and beaches. Walruses seldom go out alone, though males and females gather in separate herds. A school of walruses can have more than 100 members that communicate with clacks, whistles, roars, growls, grunts, barks, rasps, knocks and even a bell-like underwater sound. A mother has one calf every two years, born on the ice, weighing about 45-75 kg (99-165 pounds) and about 95-123 cm (3-4 feet) long. The calf often takes a ride on the mother's back and gets milk upside down when the mother is in the water.

Moving around

Walruses are pinnipeds, which means they have hairless flippers in place of limbs, like seals and sea lions. Their squarish front flippers have five fingers and help them steer in water. Their triangular back flippers also have five digits and act like a propeller. The flippers are used to walk on land. When they are tired of diving, walruses can fill up air sacs under their throat and float standing up!

The walrus has a thick wrinkly skin that acts like an armour, lending protection when it fights with other walruses

CREATURE PROFILE

Common name: Walrus

Scientific name: *Odobenus rosmarus*

Found in: Arctic region, -15-5°C (5-41°F)

Weight: Adult males: 800 1,700 kg
(1,764-3,748 pounds)

Adult females: 400-1,250 kg
(882-2,756 pounds)

Length: Adult males: 2.7-3.6m (9-12 feet) long

Adult females: 2.3-3.1m
(7.5-10 ft) long

Longevity: 35–50 years

Prey: Clams, snails,shrimps,worms, mussels and rarely,young seals

Enemies: Humans, polar bears, orca whales. Walruses were hunted extensively for fat and meat. Their tusks were used to make jewellery and artefacts

Status: Threatened—laws ensure only people native to the Arctic may hunt them. About 250,000 walruses are left, protected by laws in Russia and USA

CARIBOU

Caribou are ruminants. They are strong swimmers and can even sleep in the water. In winter, when food is snowed under, caribou shovel with their noses. Caribou are always on the move, looking for food.

Antlers for all

Caribou are the only members of the deer family in which both the male and female animals have antlers. The antlers begin to grow when a calf is just two months old. The antlers of male caribou are larger than those of the female. Their huge antlers spread about 120 cm (4 feet) across, are 125 cm (4 feet 1 inch) long and weigh 6.8-9 kg (15-20 pounds). They shed their antlers every year. From April to October, the antlers grow again from two stubs of bone or pedicles. The new antlers are covered with soft fur called velvet. The velvet is cast off when the antlers have grown.

Special hooves

Caribou have large, wide hooves that support them in the snow and in the marshy tundra. The wide hooves distribute the caribou's weight as they walk over soft snow. In summer, when the tundra is wet and soft, the hoof pads are spongy. In winter, they tighten to keep the animal from slipping. Their hooves also help them paddle when they swim. Their legs are long, slim and strong. A calf begins to run 90 minutes after its birth to keep up with the herd. Veins and arteries run close together in the caribou's long legs. This helps to keep the blood of the veins warm as well. So their legs are kept at a safe 30-50ºC (86-122ºF) and help them survive the cold.

🐾 *Caribou can travel up to 4828 km (3000 miles)!*

🐾 Caribou are herbivores and eat lichen, sedge and willow

A hearty meal

Caribou move in large herds. So, they eat up most of the food in one place and have to move on to find more food. In summer (May-September), caribou eat the leaves of the tiny willow, sedge, a grass-like plant, and flowering tundra plants. In winter, which sets in from October, most plants wither away. So, caribou have to eat lichen, dried sedge, mushrooms and small shrubs.

What a long nose!

The caribou's nose is so long that by the time the cold air from outside travels to the animal's lungs, it becomes warm. The nose also gives the caribou a strong sense of smell to make up for its poor eyesight. Although they cannot make out an enemy from a friend until they are quite close to it, their nose warns them of any danger. Then, their long legs help them to run quickly away. A startled caribou can run at 80 km/hour (50 mph). They have to keep safe from people, wolves and bears, and also golden eagles which kill newborn calves. They are also troubled by mosquitoes and warble flies and climb to higher and cooler places to escape them.

CREATURE PROFILE

Common name: Caribou

Scientific name: *Rangifer tarandus*

Found in: The Arctic tundra

Weight: Adult male: 159-182 kg
   (350-400 pounds)

   Adult female: 80-120 kg
   (175-225 pounds)

Calf: 6 kg (13 pounds)

Height: 1.2m (4 feet)

Length: 1.8m (6 feet)

Population: About 5 million

Diet: Lichen, sedge, willow

Enemies: Humans, wolf, eagle, bear

MORE ARCTIC ANIMALS

Parts of northern Asia, Europe and North America fall within the freezing Arctic region. Animals have thick coats and often change colour to blend in with the snow. Animals like skunks, bears and chipmunks hibernate in burrows during winter to conserve energy.

🐾 Despite having so much fur, the musk ox is troubled by diseases from mosquito bites on its nose

Musk Ox

The shaggy brown musk ox, which has hair even on its udders, wears one of the finest fur coats. Its 4 inch thick coat helps it survive the Arctic winter even at -34°C (–30°F). It feeds on any plant and grass it can find. Its horn covers the brain like armour. The older bull leads the group. When the enemy attacks, the ox spears it. Before a charge, it presses its nose against its knee to release the musk from a gland near the nose.

🐾 The Arctic hare's fur helps it to blend into its snowy surroundings

Arctic Hare

The Arctic hare has fur that helps it to hide. In winter, its long coat turns white. In summer, when the snow melts and the ground can be seen, it becomes greyish-brown on top. Its large feet helps it to run across the snow. Arctic hares live on rocky slopes in nests, since it is difficult to dig a burrow in the frozen Arctic ground. They eat different parts of the willow, grass, flowers and crowberries. Arctic hares gather in groups for protection. When a wolf or fox attacks, they scatter in different directions to confuse their attacker. This makes them look like big jumping snowballs. Each litter has four to eight dark-furred babies, born in June.

Wolverine

The wolverine isn't a cousin of the wolf. This shy but fierce animal is related to the weasel. It is clever and hides itself well. The wolverine, whose name means glutton, doesn't really eat more than it needs. Although wolverines hunt, they also feed off dead animals and even if they find a large animal, they eat only as much as they need. They bury the rest in the snow to eat later. They spray what is left over with musk from special glands, to warn other animals not to touch it. Their large, furry feet help them to sprint at lightning speed over the snow to catch prey. They cannot see very well, but they can chase and tire out a large prey like moose. At times they also climb on a rock and spring on the prey.

Arctic Fox

The Arctic fox lives further north than any other land mammal. It has the warmest fur of all Arctic animals. Its' fur is grey-brown in summer, when the ice melts and the ground looks blotchy, and white in snowy winter. It has a long, bushy tail. It helps the fox steer when it runs. It can change direction quickly with a sweep of its tail. The tail also helps it to keep its nose and paws warm when it curls up to sleep. An Arctic fox hunts alone, and eats lemmings and birds.

🐾 *Wolverines have a grey-brown fur with a yellowish tinge around the face and on the sides*

CREATURE PROFILE

Common name: Arctic fox

Scientific name: *Alopex lagopus*

Height: At shoulder 25-30 cm (10-12 inches)

Weight: 2.7-4.5 kg (6–10 pounds)

Colour: White in winter, Grey-brown in summer

Prey: Lemming, tundra vole, birds

ANTARCTIC MARINE LIFE

The oceans in Antarctica have four times more plant and animal life per acre than the other oceans of the world. The cold water, rich in oxygen, encourages marine life. An obvious food chain works in the oceans—larger creatures eat smaller ones.

Whales

Most of the whales found in the Antarctic in summer, head north in winter, since the water freezes over. There are two groups of whales in the Antarctic, six species of baleen whales and four species of toothed whales. Baleen is a hairy sieve in the whale's mouth. It keeps the krill, small fish and other food in and allows the water the whale gulped in with the food, to flow out. Baleens include the blue whale, the largest animal in the world. It grows up to 24m (79 feet) and can weigh 140 tonnes. Other baleens are the fin, the southern right whale, the sei, the minke and the humpback. Toothed whales eat fish and squid and include the sperm whale, the smaller bottlenose whale, and the southern four-tooth whale.

What's that light?

The first Antarctic fish was caught in 1840 during James Clark Ross's expedition. Several types of strange fish inhabit the oceans of Antarctica. Lantern fish have huge eyes and light-producing organs along their belly that attract prey. Patagonian Toothfish have a large mouth and dog-like teeth. Pouched lampreys stop feeding when they go into the freshwater to lay eggs, and die soon after their young are born. These fish eat krill, small plants and crabs.

🐾 Whales are mammals that breathe air through blow holes

Fish

About 200 kinds of fish live in the Antarctic. The largest is Antarctic cod, which grows to 1.5m (4.9 feet) and weighs 25 kg (55 pounds). Other fish include plunder fish, dragonfish, ice fish, eelpouts, sea snails, rat-tailed fish, hagfish, barracuda, lantern fish and skates. Some Antarctic fish are the only vertebrates that have no haemoglobin in their blood. This makes their blood circulate more slowly, so they can save energy. Ice fish and cod can survive in the Antarctic because they have glycoproteins or antifreeze in their blood.

Krill

Krill are tiny shrimp-like creatures. Antarctic krill is one of 85 species of krill found in the world. Krill swim in schools thousands of metres wide and look like a red wave in the depths of the sea. They rise to the surface only at night. They are important in the Antarctic food chain. Krill feed on diatoms, tiny algae that have a hard skeleton, algae and phytoplankton or tiny plants. Birds, fish, squid, seals and whales eat krill.

🐾 *Krill can exist without food for 200 days!*

CREATURE PROFILE

Common name: Krill

Scientific name: *Euphausia superba*

Length: Adults: 7-8 cm (2.7-3.1 inches)

Weight: 1 g (0.03 ounce)

Enemy: Humans, fish, birds, seals, whales

ARCTIC WHALES

Three types of whales spend their lives in the Arctic ocean: bowhead, beluga and narwhal. Their bodies have enough blubber for them to survive the icy waters of the Arctic. All whales need to have a good sense of sound since the water is too murky to see well.

Bowhead

The bowhead whale gets its name from its large, bow-shaped head that is about 40 per cent of its length. Its head is so strong that it can break through thick slabs of ice. It has a huge mouth, small eyes and large lips. Bowheads swim with their mouths open, eating along the way. A bowhead's mouth is lined with 350 pairs of black baleen plates and silver bristles. Bowheads feed mainly in summer when they swim north. They eat creatures like fish and shrimp, which are about 2.5 cm (1 inch) long. The food stays in their mouth while the water is sieved out through their baleen strainer.

Singing whales

Bowheads swim in groups of three to fifty. They normally dive for about 15 minutes and go as deep as 155m (500 feet). Bowhead whales breathe through two blowholes at the top of their head. In autumn, they move south, where their babies are born. The calf, which is 5m (17 feet) long and weighs about 4.5-5.4 tonnes is born near the surface of the water. It can swim when it is less than half an hour old. The calf feeds on its mother's milk for a year. Bowheads sing or make different sounds, which cover seven octaves. This helps them find their way and keep together. They have a 50 cm (20 inches) layer of blubber that helps them survive the winter.

🐾 Baleens are thin, long plates of keratin, the edges of which have loose threads of keratine that act as fine filter. Each species has a unique colour and size of baleen

🐾 Sound and echoes help whales to communicate, hunt and find breathing holes

58

🐾 *The Narwhal probably uses its long tusk to fight in courtship battles. It also uses the tusk to look for food. However, the tusk is not used in hunting*

Narwhal

Narwhal, in Old Norse, means corpse whale, after its blue-grey skin with white blotches. The narwhal is an unusual whale. It has such a long ivory tusk that it has been mistaken for the magical unicorn in ancient legends. Narwhals have two upper teeth. When the male is one year old, its left tooth grows spirally, twisting anti-clockwise, for about 2–3m (7–19 feet). They have a round head, a blunt snout, a small mouth and a cylindrical body covered with blubber. They live in pods of four to twenty, often in single-gender groups.

Noisy Narwhal!

Narwhals live for about 50 years. They are very vocal and noisy creatures that squeal, click and whistle to find each other and to navigate. Narwhals can dive and stay under the water for 7-20 minutes, while they look for squid, fish, shrimp and other small creatures. The calves have smooth brown skin and nurse for about four months.

CREATURE PROFILE

Common name: Narwhal

Scientific name: *Monodon monoceros*

Length: Adult male: 4.9m (16 feet)

Adult female: 4m (13 feet)

At birth: 1.5m (5 feet)

Weight: Adult male: 1,632 kg (1.8 tons)

Adult female: 1,000 kg (2200 pounds)

At birth: 80 kg (175 lb)

Population: About 45,000

Enemy: Humans, polar bear, orca, shark, walrus

Conservation status: Endangered

KILLER WHALES

Killer whales are the largest members of the dolphin family. They are found in most oceans, but mainly in the Arctic and the Antarctic. They are smaller than many whales and have a body that tapers at both ends. Killer whales live in groups or pods of about 100. Female killer whales and calves swim in the centre of the pod while males swim on the outside. They breathe through a blowhole on their head.

🐾 *Killer whales have jet black bodies with white patches around their eyes, under the jaw, belly and on its sides*

Closing in for the kill

Killer whales eat fish, squid, seals, sea lions, walruses, birds, sea turtles, otters, penguins, polar bears, and even an occasional moose. They hunt in pods, pushing their prey into a small area before they attack. They can even kill a blue whale, the largest animal on earth. Sometimes, they slide onto sandbars or ice to chase their prey. They are toothed whales. Their 40 to 56 sharp teeth, each 7.6 cm (3 inches) long, lock together. These teeth are used for tearing. They can even swallow small seals and walruses whole.

Calf care

Killer whale calves are about 2.6m (8.5 feet) long at birth and weigh between 136-181 kg (300-400 pounds). A baby can swim from the day it is born. For the first few days, the dorsal fin and tail flukes are flexible but as the calf ages, the fins grow stiff. A calf feeds from its mother for a year, although it cuts its first upper teeth at two or three months. The lower teeth appear when it is four months old and the calf starts eating fish. When it is a few days old, the calf learns to make noises, and it improves its language as it grows.

I spy!

Killer whales have good eyesight, and can hear better than humans. Their fat-filled lower jawbones help sound waves travel to their ears. Killer whales make clicking sounds and wait for the echo, so they can avoid hard objects in the dark and murky water. Their eyes are on each side of their head near a white false eyespot on their black body. The ears are small openings just behind the eyes. Their prey can mistake the eye-spot for an actual eye and attack the spot instead of the whale's eyes. Killer whales lift their heads to see above the water. They do not have vocal cords, but killer whales can make a variety of sounds like clicks, moans, grunts, whistles and squeaks.

Fast swimmers

Killer whales swim faster than most mammals, reaching speeds of 48.4 km/hour (30 mph). They can dive 30.5-61m (100-200 feet) and stay under water for four to five minutes, when their heart slows down from 60 beats to 30 beats per minute. They inhale and close the flap over their blowhole before a dive. As they reach the surface, the blowhole opens and they breathe out. A layer of body fat, which is 7.6-10 cm. (3-4 inches) thick, lies underneath the whale's skin and keeps it warm.

CREATURE PROFILE

Common name: Killer whale

Scientific name: *Orcinus orca*

Found in: Largest numbers in Arctic and Antarctic regions

Weight: Adult males: 3,628-5,442 kg (8,000-12,000 pounds)

Adult females: 1,361-3,628 kg (3,000-8,000 pounds)

Length: Adult males: 5.8-6.7m (19-22 feet)

Adult females: 4.9-5.8m (16-19 feet)

Prey: Fish, squid, seals, sea lions, walruses, birds, sea turtles, otters, penguins, polar bears

Status: With about 70,000 to 180,000 in the Antarctic alone, killer whales are not an endangered species

🐾 *Killer whales are not threatened by any natural predators and therefore can live comfortably for about 50-80 years*

🐾 *Despite being a predator and a killer, killer whale have never been reported killing a human being*

GREENLAND SHARK

The Greenland shark swims so slowly that it was named *Somniosus microcephalus* or the small-headed sleeper. Since it can live in very cold water 2-7°C (36-45°F), it is found in both the Arctic and Antarctic. Most Greenland sharks are 2.4–4m (8-14 feet) long. The largest shark ever seen was 6.5 metres (21 feet) long.

Black beauty

Little is known about this shark, since it prefers to live in deeper water than most sharks. This greyish-black shark with a short snout has a cylinder shaped body and two small, boneless fins. Its teeth, framed by thin lips, are small for such a huge animal. However the teeth make up for their lack of size by being razor-sharp. The upper teeth are long, and the close-set lower teeth are flatter. The Inuits used the upper teeth as knives, and the lower teeth to cut hair with.

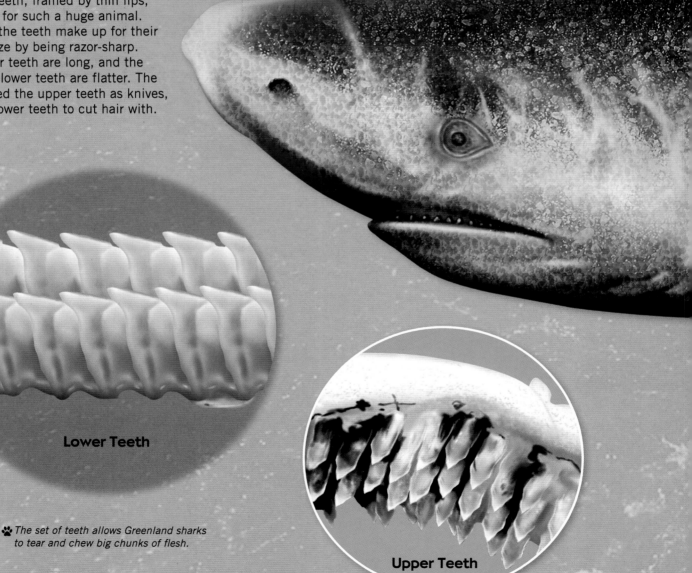

Lower Teeth

🐾 *The set of teeth allows Greenland sharks to tear and chew big chunks of flesh.*

Upper Teeth

Large family

Greenland sharks give birth to about ten pups at a time, which are about 38 cm (15 in) long. Before birth, they develop from eggs inside the mother's body. They have short, wide tails ideal for quick bursts of speed, leading some biologists to believe that these sharks are not as sluggish as first thought. In winter, they go deeper into the sea. Female sharks are larger than males. The pups grow slowly, because of the very cold water they swim in.

CREATURE PROFILE

Common name: Greenland shark

Other names: Sleeper shark, gurry shark

Scientific name: *Somniosus microcephalus*

Found in: North Atlantic Ocean

Weight: Adult 900 kg (2,000 pounds)

Length: Adult 6.5m (21 feet)

Prey: Fish, seals, porpoises, flesh of dead animals

Enemies: Humans

Status: Not endangered

❖ The flesh of Greenland sharks can be poisonous to other animals.

Unusual oil well

Greenland shark liver is full of oil for which it is hunted. One shark can produce about 114 litres of oil. This oil helps the shark stay afloat and swim. The oil, rich in vitamins A and D, is said to be good for the health. The skin of the shark was used by the Inuit to make boots.

Strange friends

Glowing light-yellow, copepods - tiny shrimp-like creatures only 3mm long (0.001 inch), stick to this shark's small eyes. Although the sharks are often blinded by the copepods, the glow from them attracts prey. The Greenland shark eats fish such as herring, eels and salmon, seals, porpoises and even dead whales. They have only once been known to attack humans. Since they swim deeper than most other sharks at 400-600m (1,300- 2,000 feet) where very little light reaches, they use their sharp sense of smell to find food. When prey is near, they inhale, and the food, up to 1m (3 feet) away, gets sucked into their mouth.

PENGUINS

Penguins are short-legged birds that can't fly. The name penguin was first given to the great auk, a bird that looked like a penguin. It is now extinct. Does *penguin* derive from the word *pinion* (pinned wing)? Or the Welsh *pen gwyn* (white head)? Or the Latin *pinguis* (fat)? No one is sure.

Only Antarctica?

There are no penguins in the Arctic, perhaps because there are more hunters there. This includes bears, wolves, foxes, rats and humans who hunted the great auk to extinction in the 1600's. Of the five species of penguins in Antarctica, the most common is the king penguin. It is the second largest in Antarctica. The Adélie penguin was named in 1840 by its discoverer, Dumont d'Urville, after his wife.

Just right for the cold

Penguin feathers are hard, small and packed closely together. The outer layer has long, smooth feathers that have a waterproof, oily coating. The inner layer of short, fluffy down traps the air and keeps them warm. Once a year, old feathers drop off or moult. When they feel hot, penguins fluff out their feathers to let air pass through. An opening for an ear is hidden under the feathers on the head. On land, penguins can't see very far. They recognize each other by their voices. Penguins rest on their belly. Adélie and emperor penguins sleep standing up when they are warming an egg. Most newly hatched chicks are covered with soft down feathers. These may be white, grey, black or brown. Since these are not waterproof the chicks must remain out of water.

🐾 *Penguins press their feet against the tail to aid in steering while they swim*

🐾 *Penguins use their small wings as flippers and paddle with webbed feet*

Look who's fishing!

Penguins catch prey with their beaks and swallow the food while they swim. They are good swimmers and can dive to 500m (1,640 feet). They can stay under water for several minutes and come up only to breathe. They have to stay safe from skuas, leopard seals and killer whales. A group of penguins is called a rookery. Male emperors that huddle together against winter storms are called a turtle, after the Roman soldiers' defensive position. Chicks group together in a crèche, which is a French word for crib. Penguins are short-legged birds that can't fly.

What a din!

Penguins are noisy, smelly birds. Adélie penguins fight for nesting sites, for rocks and pebbles to make their nests or even if another penguin comes too close to their nests. They bray, sway, pinch with their beaks and hit the enemy with their bony flippers. They steal pebbles from other nests. When the chicks grow up and the penguins leave for the sea to feed, the last adult collects and hides pebbles for the next nest. This makes a bumper prize for the penguin that arrives first to nest! Penguins are clumsy walkers and cover ground by tobogganing on their stomachs. In the water, they play by jumping out and diving back in.

CREATURE PROFILE

Penguin

Scientific name: *Spheniscidae*

Found in: The southern hemisphere, right down to Antarctica

Weight: Largest: adult emperor penguin, 27-41 kg (60-90 pounds)

Smallest: adult fairy penguin, 1 kg (2.2 pounds)

Length: Longest: adult emperor penguin 1.2m (3.9 feet)

Smallest: adult fairy penguin 41 cm (16 inches)

Prey: Fish, krill, squid, crustaceans

Enemies: Skua, leopard seal, killer whale, giant petrel, shark

Conservation status: Stable

🐾 A rookery

EMPEROR PENGUINS

The emperor penguin is the largest and heaviest penguin in the world. It has a big head with a smart, black hood, short, black wings, a blue-grey neck patch, white front, orange ear-patches and bill. Its tail is short. Emperors live throughout the year in Antarctica. They live up to 20 years.

Proud papa

The emperors are the only birds in Antarctica that breed in winter. The female lays one egg in May on the snow when it can be as cold as -62° C (-80° F). She rolls it onto the male's feet. If he cannot scoop it up, it freezes. The male incubates the egg, covering it with his brood pouch, a fold of stomach skin. To keep the eggs warm, males huddle in groups called turtles.

Crèche

Both parents feed the chick, bringing up food from their stomachs. When the chicks are seven weeks old, they join a crèche or a group of chicks. Chicks are safe and warm in a crèche. When the parents come to feed them, the chicks recognize their call. Penguin calls can be heard about a kilometre away and help them find their families.

🐾 *Emperor penguins*

🐾 *The mother leaves after laying eggs and returns after nine weeks to feed and raise the chick.*

Feast for a king

Unlike most penguins, which feed on krill or tiny shrimp, emperor penguins also eat fish and squid, which they catch in their sharp beaks. They can dive down to about 150-200m (490-650 feet), and can stay under water for five to eight minutes. One dive was recorded at 310m (700 feet), and another was 18 minutes long. That makes them the best divers among birds. Hungry chicks move their heads back and forth. When the parent looks down, the chick touches its beak and the parent feeds it.

Mother or Father?

Male and female emperors look alike. Both lose weight while they nurse the chick, so it is difficult to tell them apart. The only difference is the female's squeakier voice. Emperors have a layer of blubber or fat under their skin that keeps them warm. In the twentieth century, they were hunted for this fat. Chicks have extra down under their feathers. Emperors have more feathers than a flying bird. Their feathers are oily, smaller, stiff and are packed closely together.

CREATURE PROFILE

Common name: Emperor penguin

Scientific name: *Aptenodytes forsteri*

Found in: Antarctica

Weight: adult: Weight varies during breeding season in both male and female. Approx 27-41 kg (60-90 pounds)

Length: Adult male 120 cm (3.9 feet)
Adult female 115 cm (3.75 feet)

Prey: Fish, squid, shelled creatures

Enemies: Leopard seal, killer whale, giant petrel, shark

Population: Estimated 200,000 breeding pairs, not counting birds younger than four years

Status: Stable

The feathers help penguins wobble and slide on their bellies without getting wet

OTHER ANTARCTIC BIRDS

There are about 45 species of birds in the Antarctic, of which 35 are birds that catch their food in the sea. They find krill, squid and fish in the water. They have few enemies on land, so their young are safe. As winter ends, Adélie penguins arrive, followed by petrels and skuas. Millions of birds celebrate summer here, including cormorants, pintails, gulls, terns, sheathbills, pipits and albatrosses. Most of them fly north in winter.

🐾 *Most sea birds have waterproof feathers and a layer of fat to keep them warm*

Albatross

One of the largest birds on earth, wandering albatrosses are powerful flyers. They look for sea food near the surface of the water and can cover hundreds of miles, feeding at night. The mother lays a single egg, which is unusual for birds. Although they can live for about 50 to 60 years, thousands are killed by hunters. Wandering albatrosses get their name from their long flight, covering 10,000 km (6,213 miles) in 10 to 20 days. Some travel right around the earth. They arrive in Antarctica to breed in November, and settle in colonies on the grasslands, making nests of mud and grass. The eggs are laid in December. Parents incubate them until April, when it is winter in the Antarctic. The chicks are fed fish and squid. Albatrosses are white with black wavy lines on the breast, neck and upper back. Their bills are yellowish-pink. It takes a young bird nine years of wearing feathers of different colours to get the plumage of its parents.

🐾 *Cormorants regurgitate food to feed their chicks*

Skua

Skuas are intelligent migratory shore birds that often travel from the North Pole to the South Pole. They are the main enemy of abandoned penguin chicks and eggs. They arrive at the Antarctic in September and lay their eggs on flat ground between November and January. The parents defend their eggs. The eggs hatch in about a month, and the chicks are ready to fly off barely two months later.

Cormorant

Cormorants are diving birds. They catch fish, eels, squid and even water snakes with a swift plunge into the water. They can dive up to 12m (40 feet). Under water, their feet propel them forward. Once back on land, they spread out their wings to dry since their dark feathers are not waterproof. They have a long, thin, sharp, hooked beak and four toes on their webbed feet. Cormorants nest in colonies on trees and cliffs. The eggs are light blue. Both parents look after the young.

Petrel

The petrel is probably the most numerous bird in the world. Millions of them, especially the Wilson's storm petrel, breed in Antarctica. They have a strange way of trying to scare their enemies off—they vomit. This habit has earned them the name stinker. Petrels build nests from piles of pebbles. They are scavenger birds that eat the flesh of dead animals. Sometimes, they eat so much that they can't fly, so they vomit out some of the food they have eaten to lighten themselves before taking off!

🐾 *Skuas eat fish, squid and even waste that they can find*

CREATURE PROFILE

Antarctic birds

Prey: Squid, fish, penguin eggs, chicks, rubbish, carrion

Adaptation: Waterproof feathers, layer of fat

Threats: Humans (albatrosses get caught in the lines of fishing boats)

Status: Albatross: Threatened

🐾 *Petrels tend to fly just above the ocean waves, sometimes giving them the appearance of almost running on the waters surface*

SNOWY OWL AND FALCON

Millions of birds fly up to nest and bring up their young in the short Arctic summer. These include murres, snow geese, wagtails, sandpipers, ducks, gulls, loons, ptarmigan, gyrfalcon and snowy owls. As winter sets in, most fly to the warmer south.

Snowy Owl

Harry Potter's pet, Hedwig, is a snowy owl. These are powerful birds. The males are all white while the females and the young have some dark feathers. These yellow-eyed owls can live in the cold because of their thick feathers, which even cover their feet. Snowy owls nest on boulders or even in unused eagle's nests. The female lays between five and fourteen eggs. These are laid on alternate days. The eggs hatch five weeks later.

Good morning or good evening?

In the Arctic, where there can be days of no darkness, the snowy owl hunts at all hours of the day for lemmings and other rodents and for the young of other birds. The snowy owl has a wide variety of calls, from an alarmed bark to something like a quack and even a musical note. They clap their powerful beak to scare away their enemies. The snowy owl's life cycle is dependent on the availability of lemmings, their main food.

During winters the snowy owl, gyrfalcon, ptarmigan and raven remain in the Arctic region

🐾 *Snowy owls can live in very cold temperatures*

Gyrfalcon

The gyrfalcon is the largest falcon in the world. It is also one of the few birds whose feathers can range from a dark grey to white. The gyrfalcon is such a great hunter that in the Middle Ages, only a king was allowed to go hunting with one. It has a hooked beak and claws. They nest on ledges and even use empty nests of other birds. They lay three to five eggs that take a little over a month to hatch. The nestlings are ready to fly after about seven weeks.

Keen hunters

Gyrfalcons eat other birds, like the flightless ptarmigan and grouse, and small animals like squirrels and lemmings. They also prey on sea birds. Gyrfalcons have an unusual flight path. Just before they swoop down on their prey, they take a short flight up and then dive straight down. They are such accomplished hunters that they can grab prey even in mid-flight.

CREATURE PROFILE

Common name: Gyrfalcon

Scientific name: *Falco rusticolus*

Other names:
Adult male: Jerkin

Found in: Arctic region

Weight: Up to 2.1kg (4.6lb)

Length: 50–63 cm (20–25 inches)

Wingspan: up to 160 cm (63 inches)

Prey: Smaller birds, squirrels, lemmings

The name Gyrfalcon comes from the French gerfaucon, and is written in Medieval Latin as gyrofalco. Some say, the name comes from the Old German word giri which means greedy

FEATHERED VISITOR

Thousands of migratory birds visit the Arctic in summer to feed and nest. They take advantage of the long days when they can feed their young. Most migratory birds fly at night. Just before they migrate, they begin to get restless at dusk. This restlessness is known as *zugunruhe*. While they migrate, these birds face many dangers including bad weather. Many are also hunted down.

Tundra Swan

The snow-white tundra swan is the largest bird in the Arctic. It has a long neck, short legs, a black bill with yellow spots, and black legs and feet. When they migrate, they fly all night. By May, they settle in the Arctic and nest on islands. They often return to an earlier nest. The swans pair for life and keep each other's company throughout the year. The young are known as cygnets and it takes them a year to learn how to look after themselves. By early October, the swans are ready to leave the Arctic. They can fly at heights of 609–1,200m (2,000-4,000 feet).

Siberian Crane

The Siberian crane is a large, white bird that has a red patch extending from its bill to behind its eye. Its legs are a light red. The female has a shorter beak. They spend most of their life in and around water. They even nest in marshy wetlands. Siberian cranes eat fruit and berries, rodents, fish and insects and also dig out roots and tubers from wetlands. As part of their mating ritual, a pair of cranes will dance and bow, flapping their wings while running and jumping to impress each other.

The Arctic tern has a thin, sharp, red beak and short red legs. It calls out in a high and sharp tone

Other migratory birds that visit the Arctic include murres, snow geese and Arctic tern

🐾 The Savannah Sparrow breeds in a wide variety of habitats including grasslands and cultivated land

Savannah Sparrow

The Savannah Sparrow is a little larger than your palm. This tiny bird flies up to 9,656 km (6,000 miles) a year. The sparrows fly at night, in groups of 10 to 100, and don't need to rest for hundreds of miles. They fly to the Arctic region to nest in late May or early June. The males try to impress the females by singing for them. Many Savannah Sparrows pair for life and like to nest close to their previous nest. They nest by tunnelling through the grass in order to try and keep their chicks safe. Sadly, predators discover many of their nests.

Arctic Tern

The Arctic tern is a sea bird that lives through an endless summer. It spends May and June in the Arctic and flies off to the Antarctic, spending November and December there, where it is summer then. They travel 19,000 km (12,000 miles) each way, meaning the Arctic tern travels further than any other bird and covers the equivalent distance of travelling to the moon and back in an average lifetime! The Arctic tern hunts by plunging into the sea to catch fish and often the male will offer part of his catch to the female.

CREATURE PROFILE

Name: Arctic tern

Scientific name: *Sterna paradisaea*

Length: 30–38 cm (12-15 inches)

Weight: 900 g (1.98 pounds)

Colour: White, black head,   orange beak, black under wings

Breeding: 1 to 3 eggs

Diet: Fish, krill, insects

ENDANGERING POLAR LIFE

Every year, about 5.4 billion tonnes of carbon dioxide are released into the atmosphere. All animals breathe out carbon dioxide, a "greenhouse gas" that traps heat. Just as a greenhouse traps heat, carbon dioxide absorbs heat and doesn't let it go out into space. Many of our activities, like burning fossil fuel to run vehicles, also give off carbon dioxide. Some of it dissolves in water and some is converted into oxygen by plants and trees by photosynthesis.

Arctic

The temperatures at the poles have been rising every decade since the 1950's. In another fifty years, the poles could be 3-5 degrees warmer. This rise is causing the ice caps in the Arctic to melt and the extra water is flooding rivers and seas. Intensive crop and cattle farming contribute to the problem both by encouraging deforestation and by increasing levels of methane, another greenhouse gas. Factories produce other gases that are heating the earth. As the earth is getting warmer, tree species of the south are moving north and are beginning to take over the tundra. If the quantity of greenhouse gases is not reduced, the tundra may disappear from the Arctic in another hundred years.

Antarctic

The temperature has risen 2.5°C (4.5°F) in northern Antarctica since 1945. Permanent ice shelves are melting. Ice shelves that previously melted annually have been melting increasingly earlier in the year for the past 20 years. If this continues, the west Antarctic ice sheet may melt. This would raise the sea level by as much as 5.8m (19 feet). Many coastal areas, all over the world, would be flooded by this water, displacing millions of people and animals and destroying trees and habitats. In January 2002, the northern section of the Larsen-B ice shelf, an area of 3,250 square km (1,250 square miles), collapsed. This was the largest collapse in 30 years. The permanent ice over the surface of Antarctica has been decreasing since the 1950's.

🐾 *The increase in the level of carbon dioxide is leading to the warming up of the earth*

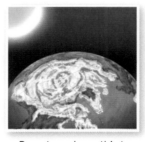 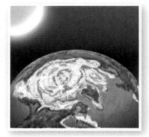 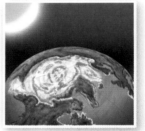

• *Departures in earth's temperature in degrees Celsius from the 1860-2000 average*

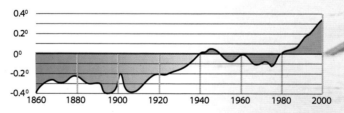

Sources: Intergovernmental Panel on Climate Change; Peter Webster et al. in Sept. 16 issue of Science.

The melting ice is not only threatening life in the poles but will also have dangerous global effects

Danger!

Polar bears walk along the ice to find food like seals, which play and live among the icebergs. Since ice in the Arctic is melting earlier than it used to, their paths are shrinking. Polar bears are 80-85 kg (176-187 pounds) lighter than they were 50 years ago because they find less food during the seven months they can feed themselves. Snow caves, where they nest, are collapsing before the cubs are able to put on enough blubber. As a result of the cold, cub deaths have risen 10 per cent in the last 20 years. In the Antarctic, Adélie penguin populations have fallen 33-50 per cent during the past 25 years since their winter homes are shrinking. While the population of seals, whales, polar bears and birds is falling, harmful insects are entering the polar regions because it is now less cold. These insects could spread disease, eat up the vegetation and destroy the ecosystem of the poles.

Recent research has proved that polar bears have grown 10 per cent thinner because the Arctic ice is melting faster each year and so the bears find it more difficult to hunt their prey

LIFE IN THE RAINFOREST

Rainforests, as their name suggests, get a lot of rain. This helps forests to grow. Rainforests are home to millions of plants and animals.

Different strata

There are distinct levels in the rainforest. Each level houses a large variety of animals. The emergent layer is made up of the tops of the tallest trees. The canopy is an umbrella of leaves. Both are home to insects, birds, reptiles, mammals and a few amphibians. The understory is the still, dark area between the floor and the canopy, home to butterflies and birds. A huge variety of creatures live on the forest floor.

Thanks to the rainforest

Rainforests have a layer of soil that is only 7.8-10 cm (3-4 inches) thick. This soil is rich with decaying leaves and dead animal matter. Tropical rainforests cover seven per cent of the earth. The trees absorb carbon dioxide and produce large amounts of oxygen, which people need to breathe. The trees also produce food like nuts, bananas, nutmeg, coffee and tea, as well as useful materials such as rubber. We get medicines from plants like periwinkle and cinchona.

🐾 *The decayed leaves and animal matter provide nutrients, retain water and replenish the soil*

🐾 *Frogs of the rainforest have smooth skin and come in brilliant colours.*

Animals of the rainforests

The rainforest has a thriving animal life. It houses more than half the world's animals. The main reasons for this are the warm temperature and ample water that enable the animals to live comfortably. Some animals have also developed unique protection methods. The walking stick insect uses camouflage and can't be seen if it stands still, while the sloth's slow pace helps it to remain unnoticed by its predators. The coral snake is so poisonous that it can kill an enemy in minutes. The hoatzin puts off enemies with a horrible smell. Beetles, wasps and millipedes fool army ants by imitating their smell to attract the ants before eating them.

🐾 *The feet of tree frogs are usually not webbed; instead they have sticky toes that help them climb trees*

🐾 *A frog climbs a tree using its specially-designed sticky toes for grip*

Plants of the rainforests

Plants use different methods to adapt to the rainforest. Orchids grow high up on trees and have aerial roots that soak in moisture from the air. Ferns grow on trees. Lianas or climbers send down aerial roots that help younger climbers. Plants need light to survive. The rainforest canopy cuts out most of the sunlight, so rainforest trees have to grow fast to get light. That is why they are tall and slender. Some of these trees, like mangroves, balance with prop roots that grow from the stem and support the tree. Huge leaves also help absorb as much sunlight as possible. Some trees have leaf stalk that turn with the movement of the sun to capture maximum sunlight.

AMPHIBIANS

Caecilians, salamanders and frogs are all amphibians of the rainforest. Amphibians breathe through their skin, so they have to keep it moist. Therefore they spend a lot of time in water.

Caecilian

The caecilian looks like an earthworm or an eel, but is neither. It is also known as rubber eel and Sicilian worm. The caecilian burrows in the moist soil of the rainforest. This vertebrate has jaws and two rows of teeth. Almost blind, it feels its way with its tentacles. The caecilian is 12.7-35.5 cm (5–14 inches) long and about 0.6-2.5 cm (0.25-1 inch) wide. It feeds on insects and worms. Its enemies are birds, fish and snakes.

Salamander

Salamanders have slender bodies, short legs and long tails. They look like lizards but have no scales. Like lizards, these vertebrates are capable of regenerating their lost limbs. Most of them do not have lungs or gills — they breathe through their moist skin. Most female salamanders lay eggs in water. Salamanders have brightly coloured coats and can be poisonous. When teased, some salamanders defend themselves by secreting poisonous liquid from their skins. Salamanders eat insects and worms. Lizards, birds and snakes feed on them.

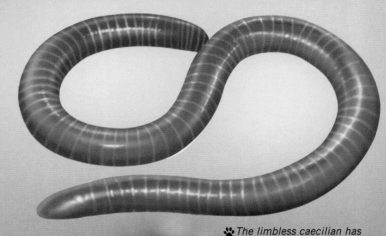

🐾 *The limbless caecilian has circular grooves on its body that make it look like an earthworm*

🐾 *The tiger salamander is mainly terrestrial and usually returns to water only to breed*

🐾 *The poison of this frog comes from eating poisonous insects*

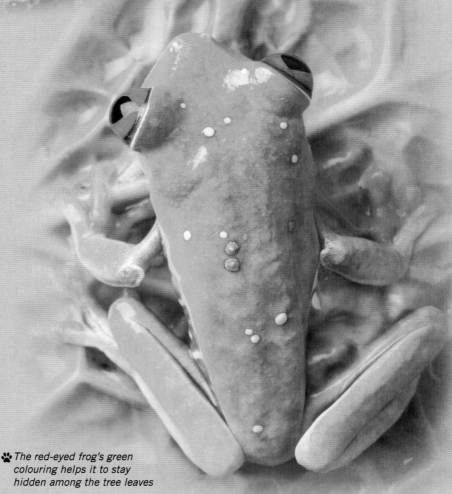

CREATURE PROFILE

Common name: Golden poison-arrow frog

Scientific name: *Phyllobates terribilis*

Other name: Poison-dart frog

Found in: Central and South America

Weight: About 28 g (1 ounce)

Feed on: Spiders, insects

Enemies: Humans

Status: Threatened due to destruction of habitat

🐾 *Most poison arrow frogs live on the ground in the leaf litter, hunting tiny insects by the day*

Frogs

Rainforests are full of unusual frogs. Frogs are the most common amphibians in a rainforest. Most of these frogs live in trees. Some look like dead leaves, so that they can hide from their enemies. Some, like the red-eyed tree frog of central America and northern South America, are active at night. Apart from their large, red eyes and red feet, these frogs are bright green with blue sides and yellow stripes. The heart and other organs of the semi-transparent glass frog can be seen through its skin!

Poison-Arrow Frog

The tiny poison-arrow frog secretes deadly poison from its back. Some people who live in the rainforest tip their arrows with this poison and use them for hunting. These frogs have bright markings on their skin to warn their predators of the danger of feeding on them. The most poisonous is the Golden poison-arrow frog of Colombia. A man can die just by licking its back with the tip of his tongue!

🐾 *The red-eyed frog's green colouring helps it to stay hidden among the tree leaves*

LIZARDS

The rainforest houses a variety of lizards like geckos, iguanas, water dragons and chameleons. These reptiles have unique adaptation techniques that help them survive comfortably in their habitat.

Basilisk

Remember the giant snake that Harry Potter kills? The crested basilisk of the rainforest is named after the same mythical monster that is believed to kill people with a glance! The rainforest basilisk is quite harmless. It is a good climber. Male basilisk have two crests on their body. Females have one. They can run across water, balancing with their long whip-like tail. Their web-like scaled toes help them tread water. Basilisks are 0.6-0.8m (2-2.5 feet) long. They eat insects, spiders and worms. They, in turn, are food for snakes and large birds.

❧ *Apart from helping to scare predators, the opened frill also helps the lizard to regulate its body temperature*

❧ *The male basilisk has two crests - one on the head the other on its back*

Chlamydosaurus

The chlamydosaurus is also known as the frilled lizard. It lives on trees in northern Australia and New Guinea. It has folds of skin around its head. When in danger, the frilled lizard opens the folds to spread its huge frill, 18-34 cm (7-14 inches) wide, to scare away its enemies. The chlamydosaurus, over 20 cm (7.8 inches) long, runs on all four limbs. When frightened, they scuttle away on their hind legs. This is why they are also called bicycle lizards. They eat insects and smaller lizards.

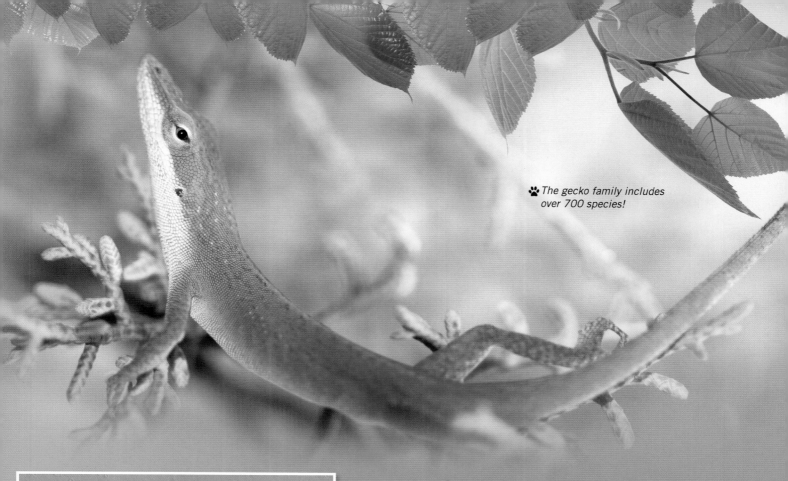

The gecko family includes over 700 species!

CREATURE PROFILE

Common name: Komodo dragon

Scientific name: *Varanus komodoensis*

Found in: Indonesia

Weight: About 135 kg (300 pounds)

Length: 2.8m (9 feet)

Feed on: Other lizards, deer, goats, wild boar and dead animals

Status: Threatened due to habitat destruction and hunting

Gecko

Geckos are the only lizards that can make sounds. They are comfortable hunting at night since they have good eyesight. Geckos eat insects and sometimes even their own eggs. Snakes are the gecko's biggest enemy. The Northern Leaf-Tailed Gecko has a large tail that looks like a leaf. Geckos are between 15-35 cm (6-14 inches) long.

Komodo Dragon

The fierce Komodo dragons are the world's biggest lizards. Komodos live in Indonesia and get their name from Komodo Island. They have strong jaws, a forked tongue and sharp claws. Active during the day, they are good runners, climbers and swimmers. They hunt all kinds of animals and sometimes even attack people. They also feed on dead animals. Komodo bites can kill because their mouth is full of deadly bacteria that poison their victim's blood.

The komodo dragon is quite agile and athletic and can run at a speed of about 18 km/hour (11mph)

CAIMANS AND CROCODILES

Caimans, alligators and crocodiles belong to the crocodilian family. These large, semi-aquatic reptiles are found in rainforests.

☙ The caiman's webbed feet and long tail help it to swim and steer well in water

Caimans

Caimans resemble alligators but are smaller and squat. Their length ranges from 1.5-2.7m (5-9 feet). There are about six sub species of caimans. The spectacled caimans are the most common. Because of their modest size, they are widely used in pet trade along with dwarf caimans. The largest are the black caimans that can grow up to 6m (20 feet) in length. These dangerous monsters are mainly found in the Amazon Basin.

Alligators

Most alligators are native to the rainforests in America, with the exception of the Chinese alligator. Alligators are excellent hunters. Their powerful vision and hearing, together with their agility helps them catch aquatic and terrestrial animals with ease. They are known to make gator holes or pools of water during the dry season.

☙ The eyes of all crocodilians are located on top of their heads enabling them to see even when they are in water

🐾 The crocodile is an ambush
   hunter — it waits for its prey
   and attacks when it comes close

Jaws of death

Crocodiles eat almost anything that they
can lay their teeth on. Their powerful
jaws and sharp, conical teeth help them
to catch and grab their prey. However,
they struggle to tear the flesh apart
and therefore swallow their food mostly
whole. Some, like the saltwater crocodile
of Australia, swim far out into the sea in
search of food. Saltwater crocodiles are
the largest reptiles on earth. These and
some other larger crocodiles like Nile
crocodiles kill humans. Some kill lions,
deer and sometimes, even sharks.

Crocodiles

Crocodiles get their name from the Greek
words *kroke* and *drilos* which mean,
worm on the pebbles. They are animals
that have survived almost unchanged
since the time of dinosaurs. Unlike other
reptiles, crocodiles have a heart with four
chambers. Crocodiles prefer slow moving
rivers and lakes and live in swamps. They
are found throughout the rainforests,
from South America to Australia.

🐾 The only creatures crocodiles do
   not kill are Egyptian plovers that
   pick the crocodile's teeth clean
   of left-over food

CREATURE PROFILE

Common name: Saltwater crocodile

Scientific name: *Crocodylus porosus*

Found in: Australia and Southeast Asia

Length: Adult male: 6-7m (20-23 feet)
          Adult female: 2.5-3m (8-10 feet)

Food: Mammals, fish, birds and even
smaller crocodiles

Status: Threatened due to habitat loss
and hunting

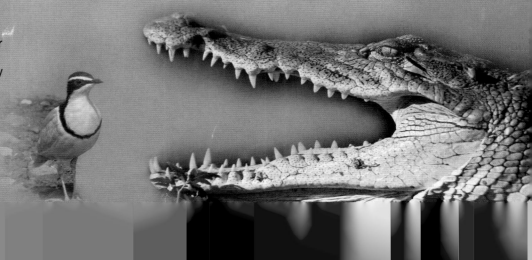

BOAS

Boas are large, non-venomous snakes usually found in the rainforests of south and central America. There are about 30 species of boas, of which the boa constrictor and anaconda are the best-known.

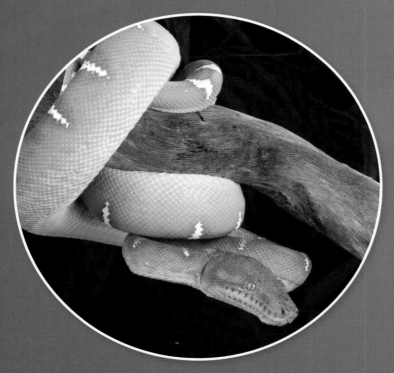

🐾 The emerald tree boa is native to South America. Its green skin helps it to blend into the rainforest vegetation

🐾 After choking its prey, the boa opens its huge mouth and swallows it, head first

Squeezing the life out

The boa is not poisonous. It kills its prey using a unique method known as constriction. The boa waits for its prey to come near or approaches it silently. It grabs the prey and wraps its body around it. The boa tightens its coils around its struggling prey, until it is unable to breathe and dies. The boa then swallows this dead victim.

Boa Constrictor

One of the better-known species of boas, the boa constrictor is found in various habitats ranging from arid deserts to wet tropical rainforests. It, however, prefers dry land or trees, and is not found near water. The boa constrictor is the second largest snake in the boa family. It can grow to a maximum length of 5.5m (18 feet). This snake feeds on large lizards, birds, rodents and small mammals. The boa constrictor is particularly fond of bats. The snake usually hangs from tree branches to grab bats that fly past. It then suffocates the prey and swallows it.

CREATURE PROFILE

Common name: Green anaconda

Scientific name: *Eunectes murinus*

Found in: The Amazon and Orinoco basins, and the Guianas in South America

Weight: Adult males: up to 135 kg 297 pounds)
Adult females: up to 250 kg (551 pounds)

Length: Adult males: 3.7-4.8m (12-16 feet)
Adult females: 6-8m (20-26 feet)

Prey: Fish, snakes, amphibians, rodents, medium-sized mammals like deer and caiman

Enemies: Humans. People kill anacondas out of fear

Status: Protected from illegal pet trade and hunting. The number of anacondas in the wild is unknown

A giant among snakes

There are four species of anacondas. Of these, the green anaconda is the most well-known. It is not only the largest of all boas, but is also the heaviest snake in the world. This gigantic snake is usually 6m (20 feet) long and weighs about 250 kg (500 pounds). Some green anacondas are believed to grow over 10m (32 feet) in length and weigh more than 500 kg (1,000 pounds)! This snake's skin is olive green in colour, with oval black spots along its body and two long stripes on its head.

An aquatic life

Anacondas are the only boas that prefer living in water to living on land. These snakes are therefore also known as water boas. Anacondas are usually found in slow-moving streams or swamps. During the day, they lie in shallow water or bask in the sun on low branches overhanging streams or swamps. Like all boas, anacondas are nocturnal and hunt mainly at night. They lie submerged with only their eyes and nose above the water. When prey comes by, the anacondas grab it with their powerful jaws and drag it underwater to drown it.

🐾 *The anaconda's nostrils and eyes are on the top of its head allowing it to see and breathe even when its body is submerged*

PYTHONS

Pythons are non-poisonous snakes found in Africa, Asia, the Pacific islands and Australia. There are about 25 species of pythons.

Largest in the world

Pythons grow for as long as they live. They range from 1-10m (3-33 feet) and weigh up to 140 kg (300 pounds). The reticulated python is the longest snake in the world. One was measured at 10m (32.9 feet). Pythons pin their prey down with their teeth, and then coil themselves around it. Like boas, they squeeze the prey tightly until it suffocates. Then, they swallow it, head-first. Pythons eat monkeys, deer, goats and other smaller animals.

Elastic jaws

The python's upper and lower jaws are attached with ligaments or bands that expand like elastic. This allows it to open its mouth wide and swallow the prey whole. The acid juices in the python's stomach digests the food. Depending on the size of the prey, the python may take over several days, or even weeks to digest it. Therefore, a python can go a long time between meals. A python that has just eaten can barely move and is often attacked by its enemies at this time.

The stretchy bands that join the python's upper and lower jaws allows it to swallow prey wider than its head

🐾 The python has four rows of teeth in its upper jaw that helps it to hold the prey but not to chew it

CREATURE PROFILE

Common name: Reticulated python

Scientific name: *Python reticulatus*

Length: 3-10m (10-33 feet)

Prey: Monkeys, goats, deer and other smaller animals

Status: Stable

Snakes with feet?

Pythons have scaly, dry skin. Most pythons have lips that can sense their prey. Unlike boa constrictors, pythons have teeth at the front and centre of their upper jaw. Snakes are believed to have descended from lizard-like creatures. Over the years, they lost their legs. However, pythons have two tiny claws at the back, where the hind legs may have been. These are longer in male pythons. Pythons, unlike most other snakes, have two lungs.

A nest for eggs

A female python lays 15 to 100 eggs. She arranges them in a pile and coils herself around the eggs until they hatch. Most pythons prefer to stay on the ground, hiding among the underbrush. Pythons are good climbers. Some, like the green tree python, live only in trees. Pythons are also able swimmers. Sometimes, pythons hide in streams with their heads above water, waiting for birds or small mammals to come to the water's edge.

🐾 The colour and patterns on the bodies of reticulated python helps it to blend into the leaf litter of rainforests

RODENTS

Rodents are mammals with two incisors or front teeth on the upper jaw and two on the lower. They get their name from the Latin *rodere* (gnaw) and *dentis* (teeth). Their teeth grow continuously to replace the parts that are worn down from their almost constant gnawing.

Agouti

Agoutis are related to the guinea pig. Agoutis live in central America, Mexico, and northern South America. They eat plants, fruits, seeds and roots during the day. As they eat, sitting up on their hind legs and holding the food in their front paws, they scatter seeds, which help new trees to grow. Agoutis have blackish-brown fur. Some have tiny tails about 2.5 cm (1 inch) long. They can run fast and swim well. When they are frightened, they freeze on the spot. Agoutis are 41-61 cm (16-24 inches) long and weigh about 4 kg (8.8 pounds). Agoutis are eaten by eagles, snakes, ocelots and jaguars.

🐾 *Agoutis feed on fruit and other parts of plants*

Coypu

This rodent has bright orange coloured front teeth. The coypu is most active at dusk or at dawn. About 40–60 cm (15-24 inches) long and weighing between 5–9 kg (10-20 pounds), the coypu has reddish-brown fur on top and grey fur below. Its long tail has little hair. Coypus eat plants and grains. Its webbed hind feet makes it a good swimmer, but it is clumsy on land. Wolves and snakes hunt coypus. The coypu is found in Asia, Europe and the Americas.

Capybara

Capybaras are the largest rodents in the world. They are found in central and South America. Capybaras live in swamps. These herbivores eat water plants, grass, fruits and grains. The brown furred capybaras are social animals and live in small groups of about six to twenty and talk to each other with barks and whistles. A female capybara gives birth to between one and six babies that are born with fur and can see right away.

Enemy!

Capybaras have many enemies like the ocelot, eagle, jaguar, and snakes like the anaconda. Even people eat them. When they sense danger, they let out a warning click, dash into the water and swim to safety. Their webbed feet help them swim well. They enjoy rolling around in the mud.

🐾 *The capybara uses water for shelter against dangers but rests on dry ground*

🐾 *The coypu is hunted for its soft, velvety under fur*

CREATURE PROFILE

Common name: Capybara

Scientific name: *Hydorchaeris hydrochaeris*

Length: 102-132 cm (40-52 inches)

Weight: 27-50 kg (60-100 pounds)

Status: Stable

OCELOTS AND JAGUARS

Jaguars and ocelots belong to the cat family. They are found in the rainforests of central and South America.

Ocelot

The ocelot looks a bit like a pet cat. However, it is a wild cat that has almost disappeared from North America. The ocelot likes to live and hunt alone. It can see well at night, which is when it usually comes out. It rests during the day. It is comfortable living and even sleeping in the lower branches of trees. However, it also hunts on the ground. Ocelots are good swimmers and great climbers.

Ocelot facts

A female ocelot gives birth to between one and four cubs. The cubs are born with their eyes closed. Ocelots often catch birds, monkeys, snakes, frogs, cattle, poultry and even fish for their meals. Ocelots are about 85-145 cm (34-57 inches) long, including the tail. Their weight is between 10-15 kg (22-33 pounds). Their unique coat, with spots and stripes, helps them hide among the trees and the undergrowth.

🐾 *The colour of the ocelot's fur ranges from tawny yellow to light grey depending on its habitat*

Jaguar

Jaguars are the third largest wild cat, smaller only than the tiger and the lion. Jaguars are heavier than leopards and have a stockier built. They are the most powerful cats in the Americas. Their tawny yellow fur have rosettes with spots inside. Jaguars have large heads and short, sturdy legs. Their muscled forearms help them drag prey more than six times their body weight.

Powerful hunter

Jaguars can climb trees and swim well. This helps them hunt a wide variety of prey. They are also fast runners. However, they don't like to give their prey a long chase. They prefer to stalk and then pounce. Jaguars feed on a wide range of animals, from deer to mice. Jaguars have a unique way of killing their prey. Unlike many other hunting animals, which bite the spine of their prey, jaguars puncture their prey's skull. This can sometimes cause them to break a tooth. Jaguars eat 5-32 kg (10-70 pounds) of flesh every day.

🐾 The mighty jaguar was a symbol of authority and military power for ancient Americans

🐾 A vigilant female Jaguar

CREATURE PROFILE

Common name: Jaguar

Scientific name: *Panthera onca*

Length: 1.62-1.83m (5.3-6 feet), excluding tail

Length of tail: 45-75 cm (18-30 inches)

Height at shoulder: 67-76 cm (27-30 inches)

Weight: 56-151 kg (124-333 pounds)

Prey: Deer, caiman, frogs, fish, cattle, mice, birds, tapir

Status: Endangered due to hunting and habitat destruction

TIGERS

The tiger is one of the animals at the top of the food chain. Tigers help maintain the balance of nature by feeding on animals that eat plants. If tigers did not eat these animals, they would eat up too many plants.

Tigers

Tigers are found in Asia. They are members of the cat family. Like other cats, they see well at night. They have claws that can be drawn back into their paws. The tiger's canine teeth are the largest among land carnivores. Tigers live alone, except when they have cubs. They mark out their territory with scratch marks on trees and with urine.

🐾 *When the cubs are two months old, the mother brings them out of the den. The cubs are very playful*

🐾 *The tiger is a good swimmer and often likes to cool off in shallow water*

Food for a king

Tigers eat animals like deer, wild boars, rabbits and cattle. When food sources are scarce, they will even eat fish and frogs. Once they spot prey, they follow it stealthily. Their padded paws make sure that they move silently. After a short dash, they pounce on the prey and bite its neck. One in every 20 chases ends in a kill. Tigers can eat 18 kg (40 pounds) of meat at a time. They can live without food for several days. A female tiger gives birth to two to four cubs, which she nurses for about six months. The cubs learn to kill their own food within 18 months.

🐾 *The Royal Bengal tiger is the national animal of India*

CREATURE PROFILE

Common name: Bengal tiger

Scientific name: *Panthera tigris*

Length without tail: 1.37-2.7m (4.5-9 feet)

Tail: 0.9-1.2m (3-4 feet)

Weight: Male 180-258 kg (397-569 pounds)
Female: 100-160 kg (220-353 pounds)

Status: Critically endangered due to habitat loss and hunting

Royal Bengal Tiger

The Royal Bengal tiger gets its name from the mangrove forests of the Sunderbans in India, where many of them live. They are also found in parts of India and Myanmar. Bengal tigers have orange fur with long vertical stripes in brown, grey or black that help them hide in the tall grass.

🐾 *Every tiger has unique stripes, like human fingerprints. Sumatran tigers have the most stripes of all tiger species*

Sumatran Tiger

The Sumatran tiger is found on the island of Sumatra in Indonesia. It is the smallest of all tigers. There are only about 500 Sumatran tigers left. These tigers can move faster than other tigers and have narrower stripes than the Royal Bengal tiger.

GORILLAS AND CHIMPS

Gorillas and chimpanzees eat fruit and help scatter the seeds. This ensures new trees grow throughout the forest.

🐾 The opposable thumbs and toes of chimpanzees help them grasp objects

🐾 Chimpanzees are good climbers and can swing from tree to tree

Chimpanzee

Chimpanzees are animals closely related to humans. There are two species of chimpanzees — the common chimpanzee and the bonobo or pygmy chimpanzee. Chimpanzees are tailless. They belong to the order of primates and are intelligent beings. Their brain is half as large as ours. Like humans, they can solve problems by using tools. They dig insects out of holes using sticks and make tools from grass stems, bark and leaves. They eat about 200 different kinds of food, including fruit, leaves, honey, ants and small birds.

Among the leaves

Chimpanzees sleep at night in nests that they build among the branches of trees. When on the ground, they walk on all fours. The arms of the common chimp are more than half its height. The shorter bonobo's arms are even longer. Mother chimpanzees have one child at a time. Chimpanzees make more than 34 different calls. Most of what we know about chimpanzees is thanks to Jane Goodall, who began studying them in Tanzania's Gombe Preserve in July 1960.

Gorilla

Gorillas are named after a tribe of hairy women called gorillai in Greek. They look fierce but are gentle and intelligent. They live in Zaire, Rwanda, Uganda, Nigeria, Gabon, Congo, Cameroon and Central African Republic. Gorillas walk on all four limbs and use the knuckles of their front limbs for support. Gorillas eat leaves, flowers, fungi and even insects.

Social animals

Gorillas live in groups consisting of as many as 30 members. Each group has one adult male or silverback, three or four adult females and their children. Female gorillas make caring mothers. Young gorillas spend about four years with their mothers. Both parents defend their children when in danger, even if it costs them their lives. Gorillas talk to each other using about 25 different sounds, from hoots to screams and barks.

🐾 *Each gorilla has a slightly different nose that helps them recognise each other!*

🐾 *The mother gorilla cares tenderly for her babies who ride on her belly or on her sides until they are about a year old*

CREATURE PROFILE

Common name: Gorilla

Scientific name: Western gorilla: *Gorilla gorilla*; Eastern gorilla: *Gorilla beringei*

Colour: Black or brownish-grey. Adult males have a silver patch on their back

Height: Adult male: about 1.7m (5.6 feet)
Adult female: about 1.5m (5 feet)

Weight: Adult male: 136-227 kg
(300-500 pounds)
Adult female: 68-113 kg
(150-250 pounds)

Status: Endangered due to habitat loss and hunting

OTHER APES

The main difference between apes and monkeys is that apes are tailless. Apes also have a better sense of sight and smell.

Gibbon

The gibbon family is rather large. It includes about nine different apes like the Siamang of Malaysia and Sumatra, the white-handed lar of Malay and the grey wou-wou of Java. Gibbons are slim and have woolly fur. They have long arms, which they use to swing from trees. They are the only apes that walk on their hind legs. Gibbons make many different sounds to communicate with each other. Gibbons eat fruits, flowers, leaves, birds, insects and eggs.

Loving family

Only six out of every one hundred animal species remain with only one partner. Gibbons are among them. The mother usually gives birth to one baby at a time, and a family of gibbons can include four children of ages up to 10 years old. Sometimes, especially at dawn, the parents break into a song and some of the children join in. The female gibbon, larger than her mate, leads the family. Gibbons do not build nests. When they sleep, they sit with their head tucked into their lap and wrap their arms around their knees.

🐾 *The slender and long-limbed gibbon can travel quickly from tree to tree*

🐾 *Gibbons have a whitish grey face ring that surrounds their black face*

Orang-utan

Orang-utan, in Malay means, 'man of the jungle'. The orang-utan is an ape from Asia and is found only in Sumatra, Indonesia and Borneo. The orang-utan has a bulky body and bow legs. This ape lives on trees most of its life and swings from one branch to another using long, strong arms. It has four fingers and a thumb that is at an angle from the fingers. Its feet have four toes plus a bigger toe that is at an angle, so they can grasp branches with both their hands and their feet. On the ground, they walk on all fours. Every evening, this ape builds a nest on a tree to rest.

A lot to eat

Orang-utans eat plants and animals. They love fruits, seeds, young shoots, fresh leaves, flowers and plant bulbs. They also eat insects, eggs, birds and small mammals. Orang-utans prefer to live alone. These intelligent animals can use tools to solve problems. Some make cups out of leaves to drink water from. Others use leaves as umbrellas. Male orang-utans have a throat pouch that helps them produce loud calls that can be heard over 1 km (0.6 miles) away.

🐾 *The mother orang-utan nurses her baby for three years*

🐾 *The orang-utan is the only big ape found in Asia*

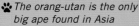

CREATURE PROFILE

Common name: Orang-utan

Scientific name:

Height: Adult male: 1-1.4m (3.2-4.5 feet)

Adult female: 0.8-1.1m (2.6-3.5 feet)

Weight: Adult male: 77-90 kg
(170-200 pounds)
Adult female: 37-50 kg
(81-110 pounds)

Enemy: Humans

Status: Endangered due to habitat loss. Baby orang-utans are sold as pets

MONKEYS

Monkeys are important to the health of the rainforests. Most monkeys help to disperse the seeds of trees when they eat the fruit, either by throwing the seeds away or passing them out with their dung.

Saki Monkey

Saki monkeys are found north of the Amazon. The male saki monkey has a white face and the female has white markings on its face. Their strong hind legs help them to leap. They eat fruits and seeds and have large canine teeth that help crack open nuts and other food. These greedy eaters also feed on small bats, squirrels and mice. Unlike most other monkeys, these monkeys live in small family groups consisting of the parent monkeys and their young ones.

🐾 *The saki monkey prefers to live in the lower canopy and the understory levels of the rainforests*

Spider Monkey

Spider monkeys are found between southern Brazil and central Mexico. They have long, slim arms and legs that lend them their name. They can take amazingly long leaps. Spider monkeys have the longest and strongest tail of all monkeys. Their tail is prehensile and helps grasp branches well. The tail acts like a fifth limb and lends support when the monkeys swing from tree to tree. While swinging through trees, they suspend their bodies, using their hands to grip one branch at a time. They eat fruits, nuts, seeds, leaves, and insects.

🐾 *The spider monkey displays great acrobatic skill while swinging from tree to tree*

CREATURE PROFILE

Common name: Howler monkey

Scientific name: *Alouatta senioculus*

Height: 0.6-1.2m (2-4 feet)

Weight: 3.5-10 kg (8-22 pounds)

Diet: Leaves, fruit, flowers insects

Status: Endangered

🐾 The tail of the woolly monkey helps it to grip branches for support when it climbs and swings through trees

Woolly Monkey

The woolly monkey has a large head and a thick body. It gets its name from the thick coat that helps keep the rain off it. The woolly monkey lives among the upper branches of trees and seldom comes down. Its prehensile tail helps it get a good grip and prevents it from falling. It has an opposable toe that helps to grasp well. Its thumb, however, isn't opposable. Woolly monkeys live in groups with membership ranging from 5 to 40. It eats fruits, leaves and insects.

Howler Monkey

The howler monkey lives in southern Brazil, northern Argentina, Paraguay and Bolivia. It is the largest American monkey. It has a large, hollow hyoid — the bone supporting the tongue. This helps the monkey produce and amplify sound. The howler monkey has the loudest roar among all land animals. Their roar can be heard more than 4.8 km (3 miles) away! It lives in the canopy of trees and spends most of its time on the tree, seldom coming down to the forest floor. It is active in the day. It feeds on leaves, fruits, seeds, flowers and insects like maggots. The tip of the underside of its tail is worn bare from gripping rough branches.

🐾 The male howler monkey is dark brown to black in colour, while the female monkey has a lighter shade of brown fur

SLOTHS

Sloth means laziness. This furry, arboreal (of the trees) mammal of the rainforest canopies of central and South America gets its name because of its slow movement.

Upside down

Sloths spend most of their lives hanging upside down from trees. They move, sleep, feed and even give birth while hanging from the trees. The only time they touch the ground is when they move to another tree. That is when their enemies like jaguars and ocelots often attack them. Sloths have thick brown fur. Some look green because of the algae on their fur. This helps them hide in the leaves. They lick their algae covered fur for nutrition.

Eat green

Sloths are herbivores or plant-eaters. They prefer to eat fresh and young leaves, but also feed on fruits and shoots. The sloth's stomach has many compartments. This helps them digest leaves, which can take a sloth almost a month. Some sloths eat insects and small lizards. Since they have no front teeth, they use their hard lips to cut leaves from branches. They eat so much that their small molar teeth get worn down but they keep growing throughout the sloth's life. Sloths do not need to drink water — they get moisture from juicy leaves and dewdrops that they lick.

CREATURE PROFILE

Common name: Sloth

Scientific name: Two-toed sloth: *Choloepus hoffmanni*

Three-toed sloth: *Bradypus tridactylus*

Lives in: South and Central America

Length: 41-74 cm (16-29 in) long

Status: Some species are endangered

🐾 The sloth's muscles are not well developed for walking upright so it spends most of its time hanging upside down from trees

🐾 The sloth holds on to tree branches with strong, hooked claws on its feet

OTHER MAMMALS

Rainforests are home to other smaller mammals too. They are usually secretive and nocturnal. This helps them hide from their predators.

Echidna

Echidnas, or spiny anteaters, were named after a Greek monster. They are toothless and feed on ants and termites. Their long snout helps them dig out food. Echidnas, like the platypus, are monotremes, or mammals that lay eggs and suckle their young. The female echidna lays one leathery egg and deposits it into a pouch on her stomach. The egg hatches in ten days. The baby, or puggle, lives in the pouch for about 50 days. Echidnas are found in Australia and New Guinea.

Tarsier

Tarsiers get their name from the long tarsus or ankle bones on their feet. They need their goggle-eyes to see while they scuttle around at night. Their long hind legs come in handy when they jump to catch an insect. Tarsiers are a little bigger than rats. Tiny as they are, they are good hunters and eat birds, lizards and snakes. Tarsiers are found in Indonesia, Borneo and the Philippine Islands.

Kinkajou

The kinkajou is an interesting mammal. This small animal belongs to the raccoon family and has the face of a bear cub, an otter-like body and the tail of a monkey! It is sometimes called nightwalker because it comes out at night to eat fruits, flowers, insects, small animals and birds. It is also called honey bear since it enjoys licking honey from hives. During the day, the mammal sleeps on trees, wrapping its prehensile tail, about 40-56 cm (15-22 inches) long, around branches so that it doesn't fall.

🐾 The echidna is covered with coarse hair and spines

🐾 Soft pads on the fingers and toes help tarsiers to grip the branches while climbing

BUTTERFLIES

Most of the butterflies in the world are found in the rainforests, especially those in South America. Peru alone is home to 6,000 species of butterflies!

Julia Butterfly

The beautiful julia butterfly or Dryas iulia has orange wings outlined in black. It has a wingspan of 82-92 mm (3.2-3.6 inches). Females are lighter in colour with more black markings. This butterfly is found from Brazil to southern Texas and Florida. It is a strong flier. Lantana and shepherd's needle are its favourite sources of nectar. The female lays her eggs on new leaves. Julia caterpillars eat these leaves.

Blue Morpho Butterfly

Blue Morpho butterflies live in Brazil, Costa Rica and Venezuela. Their wings are blue on top and brown underneath. When these large butterflies rest, the brown colour, spotted with bronze, is visible. Blue Morphos drink the juice of rotting fruit. They give off an unpleasant smell when they are disturbed. Their hairy caterpillars are reddish-brown and have light green spots on their back.

Monarch Butterfly

Monarchs are the fastest butterfly in the world. They can fly 27 km (17 miles) in an hour. Swarms of monarchs migrate every year from Canada to the rainforests of Central America. Some of them fly over 3,218 km (2,000 miles). These butterflies are poisonous because their larvae feed on poisonous milkweed. This keeps them safe from predators, who become ill and remember never to eat them again. Monarchs drink nectar from milkweed, lantana, lilac, dogbane, red clover and thistle flowers. Monarchs have a wingspan of 8.6-12.4 cm (3.4-4.7 inches).

Blue Mountain Butterfly

The blue mountain swallowtail lives in Australia, New Guinea and Indonesia. The male is a brilliant blue and black. The swallowtail gets its name from the two long tails that grow from the tips of its wings. The pupa and the caterpillar are green. These butterflies are strong fliers.

CREATURE PROFILE

Common name: Blue mountain swallowtail

Scientific name: *Papilio ulysses*

Other names: Ulysses, blue emperor, and mountain blue butterfly.

Length: 11 cm (4 inches)

Wingspan: 14 cm (5.5 inches)

Status: Not threatened

🐾 The julia butterfly has a bright orange colour and looks stunning against the green rainforest environment!

🐾 The blue morpho is a big butterfly with a wing span of 15 cm (6 inches)

🐾 A monarch butterfly drinking nectar from milkweed

OTHER INSECTS

Insects are creatures that have three pairs of jointed legs, a head, thorax and abdomen, hard outer skeleton, a pair of antennae and wings. Some, like the hummingbird flower mite, are so tiny that they can fit inside the nostrils of hummingbirds!

Beetles

There are millions of beetles in the rainforests. Jewel beetles have bright colours on their wings and shine like gems. Most of them feed on nectar while their larvae, or young, get their food by boring into wood. The black male rhinoceros beetle has one horn sticking out in front of its head. The Hercules beetle has a pincer that looks like a stinger, but it is actually only used to scare off enemies.

Bee

Of all the rainforest creatures that help pollinate flowers, bees are the busiest and most important. Many of them, like the tiny tube bees, do not sting. They sip sweat off humans so are also called sweat bees. Other bees do not bother to gather pollen. Instead, they feed on dead animals. Some bees make their nests from plant resins they collect from the nests of other bees.

Ants

There are more ants than mammals in the rainforest. About three out of every ten creatures in the Amazon basin are ants. They make up 86 per cent of the animals found at the canopy level. In Peru, 43 different species of ants were seen on one tree alone. One single colony can house millions of residents. These include the queen ant, the males and an army of female workers who have no wings. The queen ant lays over 100 million eggs in a day!

CREATURE PROFILE

Common name: Leafcutter ants

Scientific name: *Atta cephalotes* (24 species); Atta (15 species)

Found in : Central and South America

Productivity: Can strip bare one lemon tree in a single day

Enemy: Phorid fly

Status: Found in plenty

🐾 Ants help clean the forest floor of dead and dying insects

🐾 The distinctive colour and spots on the ladybird are meant to make them look unappealing to predators

MACAWS AND TOUCANS

Rainforests are teeming with birds that live in the two upper levels — the tallest branches and the canopy. Many, like the macaw and toucan, have developed special traits that help them live there.

❧ Toucans are found only in the rainforests of the Americas

Toucan

The toucan makes a noise that sounds like some one trying to say, 'RrrK!' Toucans have enormous bright beaks, a rounded tail and squat bodies. The beak, in some of the 40 species, is more than half the length of the body but is light. The beak edge is cut like a saw. Unlike the macaw, toucans have a slim, frayed tongue.

Macaw

Macaws belong to the family of birds called Psittaciformes. They get this name from the pigment, psittacin, which gives them their brilliant colours. The 17 species of macaws are related to parrots and have a strong beak that curves down. The tip of their upper beak is sharp, to rip and tear with. Macaws eat fruit, seeds and nuts. The macaw has a long tail. However, it has fewer, stronger feathers than most other birds. The hyacinth macaw, 100 cm (39.4in) in length, is the largest in the world. The smallest, the northeastern macaw of South America, is one-third its size.

Toucan facts

Toucans eat fruits, insects, bird eggs and even small birds. They eat a fruit whole and then bring up the seeds. They lay a clutch of between one and four eggs in a hole in a tree trunk. Both parents take turns to help the eggs hatch and feed the chicks. Toucans are poor flyers, so they hop to get around.

Social birds

Macaws are social birds and choose their partners early in life. If one dies, the other frets and often does not live very long. Macaws nest in tree hollows. Macaws are noisy, intelligent birds that can imitate well. This makes them popular pets. This has led to several species like the Spix's macaw becoming extinct in the wild.

CREATURE PROFILE

Common name: Toco toucan

Scientific name: *Ramphastos toco*

Diet: Fruit, insects, eggs, small birds

Length: 18-63 cm (7-25 in)

Status: Stable

❧ The macaw's feet have two toes in front and two at the back that gives them a good grip

OTHER BIRDS

Rainforests are home to a large variety of birds. Some can fly well, others not so well. Some are completely flightless and hop to get around.

Quetzal

The quetzal is a large, colourful bird of South America. The male is about 35 cm (14 inches) in length and has a green tail 61 cm (24 inches) long. The quetzal lives alone and cannot fly well. This makes them an easy target for eagles and owls. It lays one or two blue eggs in the hole of a tree. Both parents incubate the eggs, which hatch in about two weeks. The male quetzal is a wonderful father and feeds its young if the mother is not around. The quetzal eats fruits, snails, frogs and insects.

The quetzal has a beautiful tail about 1 m (39 inches) long

Trogon

Trogons are found in most rainforests, especially in central and South America. They get their name from the Greek word for nibbling. These birds nibble away at trees to make a nesting hole. Their first and second toes face backward, unlike most other birds, whose first and fourth toes face the back. This makes their grip weak. Trogons have a short, broad bill. They eat fruits and insects and live mostly in trees.

A white tailed trogon

Jabiru

The jabiru ('swollen neck.') stork is one of the largest birds. Its heavy bill helps it catch frogs, snakes and fish. It lives in large groups in marshes or near lagoons. The jabiru is found from southern Mexico to northern Argentina. In November, this bird nests in tall trees. By July, the young are ready to fly north with their parents.

Cassowary

Cassowaries are flightless birds of Australia and New Guinea that run at 48 km/hour (30 mph). Cassowaries kick in self-defence with powerful legs that end in three-toed feet with sharp claws. The middle claw is 12 cm (5 inches) long and can rip an enemy apart. Cassowaries have a bony crest on their head which they use to clear a path through the forest. Their feathers look like a shaggy wig. Cassowaries eat fruits, insects, frogs and even snakes.

The cassowary helps to disperse seeds throughout the rainforests

RAINFORESTS IN DANGER

Rainforests have existed for millions of years. Sadly, over the last few centuries, man has been cutting them down. Rainforests once made up 14 per cent of the earth's land surface; now they cover only 6 per cent. Rainforests are home to thousands of plant and animal species. Experts say that the rainforests could be gone in less than 40 years.

We increase, animals decrease

About one-and-a-half acres (65,000 square feet) of rainforest are cleared every second to make room for the growing human population. The twentieth century saw more people born than ever before. In 1800, the population stood at about one billion, and by 1950, it was 2.6 billion. Today, it is 6.5 billion; while the animal population is dwindling fast because their homes are being cut down.

A matter of more concern

Rainforests are cut down because people need more space to live, more wood to build houses and make furniture with, and more land to grow crops on. Therefore, rainforest animals and birds lose their homes and die. Animals like tigers, pythons, monkeys and birds are killed for their skin, fur and feathers. Some people make jewellery out of animal teeth and claws. In some places, animal body parts are used for traditional medicine. Parrots, macaws and pythons are sold illegally as pets, and they seldom survive or have babies outside the rainforest.

Around the world

Deforestation, affects the whole world in more ways than we apprehend. If there are fewer trees to absorb greenhouse gases like carbon dioxide and methane, the earth becomes drier and hotter. This may cause the ice at the north and south poles to melt, causing rivers and seas to overflow. This will lead to large scale destruction of life and property. When forests are cut down, more soil gets eroded since rain falls directly onto the ground, and there are no roots to hold the soil. With fewer forests, there will be lesser rain, which will in turn have a harmful effect on the earth's climate.

The humming bird may have no home to spend the cold winter season in and may therefore die

People have cut forests extensively to make homes for themselves

LIFE IN THE SAVANNAHS

Most of us would love to go on a safari to see wild animals in their natural habitat. The best place for that would be a savannah. A savannah is a large area of land filled with tall grass and very few trees. Savannahs are also known as tropical grasslands and are found on the edges of rainforests. They cover parts of India, Australia, South America and almost half of Africa.

Weather watch

Savannahs are warm throughout the year. Temperatures vary between 20°C-30°C (68°F-86°F). There are only two seasons in the savannahs — a dry winter season that lasts for 4-6 months and a wet summer season that lasts for about eight months. Most savannahs receive a lot of rain during the summer. It can get very hot and humid during these months. The dry winter months are much cooler, but are marked by drought and fire. Wildfires are necessary to maintain the savannahs, because otherwise the trees would multiply and ultimately cover the grasslands.

Plants of the savannahs

Savannahs are dominated by tall grasses, such as star grass, lemon grass, Rhodes grass, elephant grass and shrubs. Savannah grasses are usually coarse and grow in tufts with bare ground in between. Trees can be seen scattered around the region. African savannahs are characterised by the presence of baobab and acacia trees.

Animals of the savannahs

More than 40 types of hooved mammals, such as antelope, zebras, hippopotamuses, rhinoceroses and giraffes inhabit the savannahs. Around two million herbivores and about 500 species of birds live in the Serengeti Plains of eastern Africa alone. Apart from the plant-eaters, savannahs are also home to large carnivores such as lions, cheetahs, leopards, hyenas and wild dogs. A huge variety of reptiles can also be found here.

Savannah survival tricks

Savannahs are dry regions with very limited water resources during winter The plants and animals here are specially adapted to deal with water shortage. Savannah grasses grow quickly in the wet season. During the dry season, these grasses turn brown to reduce water loss. They store necessary water in their roots for the dry season. Baobab trees produce leaves only in the wet season. They also store water in their trunks The acacia has long taproots that can reach water deep in the ground.

🐾 *Fires are necessary to the savannahs, but they must not get out of control*

🐾 *The African savannah offers the best safari because it is teeming with animals and there are not many trees to block the view*

KING OF THE SAVANNAHS

An angry lion is among the most dangerous animals in the world

The lion is known as the 'king of beasts' for a good reason. It is the most majestic and powerful of all cats. Its loud roar reflects its immense strength.

Life in the savannahs

Lions are usually found in the open grasslands. They are not found in deserts or thick forests. Their brownish yellow coat helps lions to blend into their surroundings. However, the male lion's magnificent mane gives it away. This is one of the reasons why male lions are not as successful at hunting as lionesses. There are two kinds of lions — African and Asiatic. The African lion is found in the African savannahs, while the Asiatic lion is limited to the Gir Forests of western India, in the state of Gujarat.

The mane story

The male lion is the only big cat with a mane. It uses its mane to attract female lions and scare its competitors. The colour and size of the mane determines the lion's strength. Lions with darker and longer manes are more mature and stronger. However, the thick mane exposes the lion to its prey when it hunts. It also increases the body temperature of the lion, making it uncomfortable at times in its warm habitat.

CREATURE PROFILE

Common name: Lion

Scientific name: *Panthera leo*

Found in: Central Africa and Gir Forest in India

Size: Adult males: 150-250 kg
(330-550 pounds)
Adult females: 117-167 kg
(257-370 pounds)

Status: Endangered. There are only about 300 Asiatic lions and about 30,000 African lions in the wild

A group of lionesses and a lion at a watering hole

LEOPARD

Leopards are the third largest of the big cats, after tigers and lions. They are excellent climbers and spend most of their time up on trees. They are also extremely adaptable and can live in a wide range of habitats ranging from the African savannahs to the thick forests of Asia.

🐾 The agile leopard is one of the cleverest hunters in the wild

Spotted wonder

The leopard is best known for the dark rosette markings on its light tan-coloured coat. The spots provide the cat with excellent camouflage in a wide range of habitats. The spots are especially helpful when the leopard is up a tree as they help to hide it well against the branches.

Arboreal life

Leopards love to climb trees. They spend a large part of their lives in the treetops. These cats even carry their prey up the trees so that they can eat in peace. This way they are able to stop hyenas from stealing their kill. Leopards have powerful shoulder and chest muscles that help them to drag prey three times their size up a tree.

CREATURE PROFILE

Common name: Leopard

Scientific name: *Panthera pardus*

Found in: West and South Africa, Middle East, India, Pakistan, Nepal, Java, Sri Lanka, China, Siberia and most of Southeast Asia

Size: Adult males: 30-70 kg
(65-155 pounds)

Adult females: 20-50 kg
(45-110 pounds)

Status: Most of the sub-species are listed endangered. The Amur leopard of Siberia is the most endangered, with hardly 50 individuals existing today.

🐾 A leopard drags its kill up the branches of a tree

CHEETAH

The cheetah is a unique member of the cat family. It is the only cat that, while hunting, regularly relies on speed rather than stealth. The cheetah is the fastest animal on land over short distances. The magnificent cheetah can reach speeds of about 113 km/hour (70 mph)!

❧ A cheetah runs down its prey and makes a kill

Not a big cat?

The cheetah is commonly referred to as a big cat. However, unlike the true big cats, such as lions and tigers, cheetahs cannot roar. Instead, they purr like domestic cats. Cheetahs are also much smaller in size and are diurnal as they rely on sight and not smell while hunting. The cheetah is the only cat with semi-retractable claws — meaning that the claws are only partially withdrawn in the paw. Despite these differences, the cheetah is often regarded as the smallest member of the big cat family.

Built for speed

Every part of the cheetah's body is adapted for speed. The cat has a narrow, lightweight body with long, slender legs and a flexible spine. It also has a small head, a flat face and enlarged nostrils that help the cat to breathe in more air while running. It also has a powerful heart, enlarged lungs and an oversized liver. The cheetah's strong paws give it a good grip on the ground. The long, muscular tail of the cheetah helps the cat to keep its balance, especially when making quick turns.

CREATURE PROFILE

Common name: Cheetah

Scientific name: *Acinonyx jubatus*

Found in: Africa and Iran

Total body length: 112-135 cm (45-55 inches)

Tail length: 65-84 cm (26-33 inches)

Status: Threatened. Fewer than 12,500 cheetahs remain in the wild today

❧ When the cheetah sprints, its spine acts like a huge spring helping it to gain speed

ELEPHANT

Elephants are the world's largest land animals. They are bulky and strong and have no natural predators. There are two kinds of elephants — the African and Asian.

Size matters

The African and Asian species are very different from each other. Both have distinct features and are easily identified. The African species are much larger than their Asian relatives. They also have less hair on the body. However, the most distinguishing feature of the African elephant is its huge, fan-shaped ears. Moreover, both male and female African elephants have tusks, whereas only the males of Asian elephants have tusks.

Of tusks and trunk

The trunk is a combination of the nose and the upper lip. The elephant uses its strong, flexible trunk to carry objects, break-off branches and pluck leaves and also to drink water. The nostrils at the tip of the trunk help to smell. The elephant waves its trunk about to capture a scent. The trunk is then placed in the mouth to identify the scent. The tusks are actually elongated incisor teeth. They are used for various purposes, from digging for food and water to territorial fights and defence.

🐾 The distinct African tusker

CREATURE PROFILE

Common name: African Elephant

Scientific name: *Loxodonta africana*

Found in: Sub-Saharan Africa

Size: Weight: 7,000-10,000 kg
            (15,000-20,000 pounds)

Height: 3-3.5m (10-11.5 feet)

Feed on: Branches and leaves

Enemies: Humans. Elephants are killed for their tusks

Status: African elephants are considered to be threatened

🐾 A herd of Asian elephants approaching a watering hole

RHINOCEROS

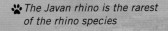

The rhinoceros is a hooved mammal that is found in parts of Asia and Africa. There are five species of rhinoceros: the Sumatran, Javan, Indian, and the white and black rhinos of Africa.

The Javan rhino is the rarest of the rhino species

Common features

The different species of rhinoceros have some features in common. They have thick skin with folds. They also have short, thick legs and a tiny tail. Most rhino species have one large horn above the nose with a smaller one behind it. Rhinos prefer to live alone and come together only during the mating season. Mother rhinos stay with their calves until they are old enough to take care of themselves.

The Asian rhinos

The Indian rhinoceros, or the great one-horned rhino, is the most numerous of the three Asian species. It is found in Nepal and the state of Assam in India. Each Asian species has unique features. The Indian and Javan rhinos have only one horn, while the Sumatran species, the smallest of all, is the only rhino with thick fur. The Sumatran and Javan species are the most endangered of all rhinos. There are only about 100 Javan and 300 Sumatran rhinos in the world today.

The African rhinos

The white rhino is also known as the square-lipped rhino. It is found in north-eastern and southern Africa. This species has a wide mouth that helps it to cut grass. It has two horns on its snout and a hump on the back of its neck. Compared to the white rhino, its black counterpart is smaller and does not have a hump on the neck. The black rhino has a pointed, prehensile upper lip that is ideal for grabbing leaves.

CREATURE PROFILE

Common name: Black rhinoceros

Scientific name: *Diceros bicornis*

Found in: Eastern and central Africa

Height: 1.4-1.7m (4.5-5.5 feet)

Weight: 800 -1,400 kg
(1,700-3,000 pounds)

Status: Endangered. Hardly 3,500 black rhinos exist today

A two-horned rhino with her calf

HIPPOPOTAMUS

Hippopotamus means 'river horse' in Greek. The hippopotamus belongs to a group of hooved mammals called artiodactyls. The animals in this group have two or four toes. The Hippopotamus has four toes. It is a plant-eating, water-loving giant.

Hippo facts

Hippopotamuses are found only in parts of Africa. There are two species of hippopotamus — the common and the pygmy hippopotamus. The common hippopotamus is one of the largest land mammals. It is around 1.5m (5 feet) tall and weighs about 4,000 kg (8,800 pounds). The pygmy hippopotamus, on the other hand, is only 75 cm (30 inches) tall and weighs about 180 kg (400 pounds).

Adapted for water

Pygmy hippos prefer to stay near water rather than in it. Common hippos, however, spend a great deal of time wallowing in water. They usually spend their days in water and come out in the morning and at nights to feed. Their eyes are positioned on top of the head. This helps to keep the eyes above the water when the hippo is submerged. Its nostrils are sealed whenever it dives underwater. Hippos can remain submerged for up to half an hour, though they prefer not to stay submerged for more than about five minutes.

Natural sunscreen!

The skin of a hippo has very little hair. Common hippos have coppery-brown skin, while pygmy hippos are greenish black in colour. The pores in the skin of a common hippo secrete a fluid which acts as sunscreen lotion, absorbing harmful ultraviolet rays and preventing the skin from cracking in the heat.

🐾 *Male hippos can be very aggressive when protecting their territory*

🐾 *The red pigment protects the hippo from disease-causing bacteria*

CREATURE PROFILE

Common name: Common hippopotamus

Scientific name: *Hippopotamus amphibius*

Found in: Central, western and southern Africa

Size: Weight: 1,500-4,000 kg
                (3,300-8,800 pounds)

Length: 3.5m (11 feet)

Status: Threatened

ANTELOPE

The term 'antelope' is used to refer to a group of plant-eating hooved mammals that are related to cattle and goats. There are at least 90 varieties of antelope. The smallest of these is the royal antelope, while the giant eland is the largest species.

The gemsbok oryx has a pair of distinctive spear-like horns

Common features

All antelope have light, slender bodies covered with thick, short fur. Most antelope are sandy brown in colour, but there are exceptions such as the gemsbok, which has grey and black fur. They have cloven hoofs and short tails. They have strong hindquarters, long legs and powerful muscles, that help them run fast. Running antelope look as if they are bouncing up and down. Antelope are also excellent jumpers, but not good at climbing. Both male and female of most antelope species grow horns. The male's horns are typically larger.

Sensing danger

Antelope are highly alert creatures. They have keen senses that help them identify danger early. Their elongated pupils give antelope a broad view of their surroundings. Their senses of hearing and smell are also excellent, helping the animals to sense danger even in the dark. They usually warn one another with various calls. Some antelope bounce up and down, keeping their legs straight. This display is known as 'stotting' or 'pronking'.

CREATURE PROFILE

Common name: Giant eland

Scientific name: *Taurotragus derbianus*

Found in: Many parts of Africa, especially Sudan, Senegal and central African Republic

Height: 1.5-1.75 cm (4.9-5.7 feet) at the shoulder

Weight: 500-900 kg (1,100-1,900 pounds)

Status: Endangered

A herd of antelope

WILDEBEEST

The wildebeest is a large hooved mammal found only in Africa. It is also known as gnu. There are two species of wildebeest — the black wildebeest or white-tailed gnu and the blue wildebeest, also known as the brindled gnu.

Blue wildebeest

Of the two types of wildebeest the blue wildebeest is larger and more common. It has a box-like head with large curving horns that expand sideways, similar to cows, and a stiff black mane. Both male and female wildebeest have horns. Its light grey to bluish-grey colour gives the species its name. Dark brown stripes run down the neck to the middle of its body.

Black wildebeest

This species is endemic to savannahs of southern Africa. It has a dark brown to black body. Its distinguishing feature is its distinctive white tail and the shape of its horns. Its horns expand forward towards its face and then curve upwards in a 'U' shape. It has a bristly mane that is cream to white in colour and black at the tips.

Bullfights

Male wildebeest, or bulls, are highly territorial. Dominant adult males mark their territories with urine, and by scraping the ground with their hooves. Two males fight over a territory or a female.

🐾 *A herd of blue wildebeest*

🐾 *The black wildebeest has a blackish-brown body*

CREATURE PROFILE

Common name: Blue wildebeest

Scientific name: *Connochaetes taurinus*

Found in: Southern parts of Africa

Height: About 1.4m (4 feet) at the shoulder

Weight: 120-270 kg (265-595 pounds)

Status: Low risk

ZEBRA

Zebras are horse-like animals with black and white stripes on their bodies. There are three main types of zebra — plains, mountain and Grevy's zebra. They are found in various parts of Africa. The black and white stripes act as a camouflage.

Coat of many patterns

The stripes vary with each species of zebra. The mountain zebra has a white belly with black stripes that are narrower than those of a plains zebra. The stripes on the plains zebra bend backward toward the rump to form a 'Y' shape on its flanks. The Grevy's zebra, the largest of all zebra species, has an erect, stiff mane, longer than the mane of any other species. The stripes on the Grevy's zebra are narrower and more closely set and do not extend to the belly. The stripes form a gleaming white patch of white on either side of the tail. The stripes also vary with each individual.

A herd's life

Zebras form small herds of about 20. A male zebra leads the herd. Mares remain with the herd for life, while foals leave the herd once they are old enough to start a herd of their own.

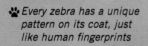
🐾 Every zebra has a unique pattern on its coat, just like human fingerprints

CREATURE PROFILE

Common name: Grevy's zebra

Scientific name: *Equus grevyi*

Found in: The grasslands of southern and eastern Africa

Height: 1.4-1.6m (4.6-5.2 feet) at the shoulder

Weight: 350-450 kg (772-992 pounds)

Status: Endangered

🐾 A zebra herd always has a lookout while the rest drink water

GIRAFFE

The giraffe is the tallest animal on land, with a height of about 5.5m (18 feet). It's famous for its extra long legs and neck. This amazing hooved mammal is found in eastern and southern Africa— Angola and Zambia in particular. They roam in the savannahs and open woodlands.

🐾 The giraffe's tongue has special protection against the acacia thorns

Reaching up

The giraffe's neck alone is 1.8m (6 feet) long — that is the height of an adult human being! A giraffe has only seven vertebrae or bones in its neck — the same as humans. But its vertebrae are much longer and are separated by highly flexible joints. Its long neck helps the giraffe reach up and pluck leaves from higher branches of trees.

A thorny diet

A giraffe eats a lot to gain energy for its daily routine. An adult giraffe can eat more than 60 kg (132 pounds) of leaves every day. Although a giraffe can eat any kind of vegetation, its favourite food is the leaves of the thorny acacia tree. The long thorns of the acacia stop most animals from eating its leaves, but not the giraffe! Its tongue, about 45 cm (18 inch) long, is covered with small bumps called papillae that protect it from the thorns. The giraffe's mouth also produces thick, sticky saliva that coats the thorns that may be swallowed by accident.

Giraffe movements

The body of the giraffe may be shorter than other hooved animals, but its long legs more than make up for this. The front legs are slightly longer than the hind legs. A giraffe has a peculiar way of walking called 'pacing'. A giraffe can run at speeds of about 48 km/hour (30 mph).

🐾 Giraffes have distinctive ways of walking, running and even drinking water!

CREATURE PROFILE

Common name: Giraffe

Scientific name: *Giraffa camelopardalis*

Found in: Parts of Africa

Height: Adult male: up to 5.5m (18 feet)

Adult female: up to 4.3m (14 feet)

Tail length: 2.4m (8 feet)

Status: Low risk.

HYENA

The hyena is the most commonly found carnivore in the African savannahs. There are four different types of hyena - aardwolf, spotted, striped and brown hyena. Of these, the spotted hyena is the best-known and most abundant species.

Spotted hyena hunt prey to a greater extent than the other hyena species

Hyena facts

Hyena can be light to dark brown or even grey in colour, depending upon the species. They have compact bodies with small heads. Their jaws are powerful enough to crush even the largest of bones. Their front legs are longer than the back legs. Hyena are very intelligent and this can be seen in their unique hunting tactics. Contrary to popular belief, not all hyena are scavengers. The brown and striped hyena are the true scavengers of the family. The spotted hyena is an aggressive hunter, while the aardwolf feeds on insects.

Living in clans

Spotted hyena live in large clans of up to a hundred individuals. A dominant female leads the clan. Unlike many other animals, the female hyena is bigger than the male. The clan size depends on the availability of prey. The larger the number of prey, the bigger the clan is. Hyenas are extremely territorial and can get very aggressive and ferocious while defending their territory.

Thinking hunters

Spotted hyena are very successful hunters. Their hunting style depends on the availability and size of prey. In places where there are not enough animals to prey, the clans are small, usually consisting of 7-10 members. In these places, an individual hyena often hunts down smaller animals on its own. However, if there is an abundance of prey, hyena hunt in packs. The hunting style also depends on the size and behaviour of the prey. When hunting wildebeest, hyena form small packs.

CREATURE PROFILE

Common name: Spotted hyena

Scientific name: *Crocuta crocuta*

Found in: Africa

Length: 1.2-1.5m (3.9-5 feet)

Weight: 40-75 kg (90-165 pounds)

Prey: wildebeest, gazelles, zebras and other hooved animals

Enemies: Lions and humans

Status: Low risk

Hyena cubs stay close to their dens so that they can run to safety in case of danger

CANINES OF THE SAVANNAHS

Many canines live in the savannahs. These include jackals and wild dogs. There are three different species of jackals in Africa. They are the golden, side-striped and black-backed jackals. The African hunting dog is on the verge of extinction.

CREATURE PROFILE

Common name: African hunting dog

Scientific name: *Lycaon pictus*

Found in: Africa

Height: 60-76 cm (24-30 inches)

Weight: 25-32 kg (55-70 pounds)

Status: Endangered. there are about 5,600 hunting dogs in the wild

Jackal

All jackals have dog-like features and a bushy tail. They have long legs with blunt feet that help them to run long distances. They are nocturnal animals, active during dawn and dusk. The species differ from one another mainly in colour. The golden jackal is sandy brown in colour, while the side-striped jackal has black and white stripes along the sides of its body.

A jackal's life

Jackals usually live in pairs or small packs of about six individuals, but single jackals can also be seen. A pack usually consists of a male, a female and their young. Male and female jackals mate for life. Jackal pairs are highly territorial. Both female and male jackals defend their territories fiercely. Jackals communicate with one another using yipping calls. Members of a family only respond to the calls of their own family. They usually ignore the calls of other families or individuals. Although they are known to be scavengers, these animals are excellent hunters.

❧ The African hunting dog is on the verge of extinction

African hunting dog

The African hunting dog is a very intelligent animal. This canine has long legs with four toes on each foot. The most distinguishing feature of a hunting dog is its colourful coat and large bat-like ears. It also has powerful jaws that can tear even the thickest hide. Hunting dogs usually form packs of 6-20 individuals. The pack consists of a main breeding pair and several non-breeding adult male helpers.

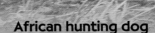

❧ The black-backed jackal is rust coloured with a patch of black hair on its back.

BABOON

Baboons are one of the largest species of monkeys in the world. These ground-dwelling monkeys are very common throughout Africa. There are five main types of baboons. They are olive, Chacma, Guinea, yellow and Hamadryas baboons. Except for the Hamadryas baboons, the rest are collectively known as savannah baboons.

🐾 Like all primates, baboon mothers are fiercely protective of their babies

Common features

All baboons have a long muzzle that looks like the muzzle of a dog. Their eyes are set close to each other and they have powerful jaws. The body is covered with thick fur. Baboons have rough skin on their bottoms. These hairless pads of skin provide comfort while sitting. Both male and female baboons differ greatly in size and colour. Males are larger than females.

Trooping in

Baboons live in groups known as troops. A typical troop consists 50 including about eight males and twice as many females and young. The savannah baboon troops are usually led by a dominant female. The males in a troop are often responsible for defending the troop members. The troop sleeps, travels and looks for food together and do mutual grooming.

Baboon behaviour

Baboons are omnivorous. They forage for food through the day. Females carry their newborn. Although it is the female who looks after the young, male baboons are known to help. They do so by gathering food for the young and even playing with them.

CREATURE PROFILE

Common name: Hamadryas baboon

Scientific name: *Papio hamadryas*

Found in: Africa and Arabia

Weight: Adult males: 15-20 kg
(33-40 lbs)

Adult females: 8-13 kg
(19-27 lbs)

Enemies: Leopards, cheetahs and humans. Baboons are considered to be agricultural pests and are therefore killed in large numbers

Status: Listed as near threatened

🐾 While on the move, baboons will often stop to groom one another

OTHER MAMMALS

Apart from antelope, big cats, baboons and hunting dogs, the savannahs are home to a wide range of animals, some of which remain a relative mystery to us. Others - like vervet monkeys, servals, caracals, gazelles and warthogs - have names you might recognise but probably don't know much about.

Vervet monkeys

These small, black-faced monkeys are found in a variety of habitats outside rainforests. They, however, prefer acacia woodlands bordering savannahs. Therefore, they stick to woodlands with streams or lakes nearby. Like all monkeys, vervet monkeys live in troops of 10-50 individuals. A troop mainly consists of adult females and the young. Adult males move in and out of these troops. The most unique behaviour of vervet monkeys is the different calls they use to indicate different types of predators. When a member produces the eagle call, the rest of the troops hide among dense vegetation.

Servals and caracals

Servals and caracals are species of wild cats that lead solitary, secretive lives. Both cats have small, slender bodies and long legs. Their heads are small with a long neck and large ears. The caracal has tufts of black hair at the top of its ears. Both servals and caracals hunt at night and therefore rely mainly on sound to locate their prey. Once the prey is located, the cat moves silently towards it and pounces on it. Servals often play with their victims before eating them. Caracals are known for their exceptional skill at bird hunting. They reach out and use their front paws to snatch a flying bird, and sometimes even more than one bird at a time.

Warthogs

The warthog is the only wild pig that is able to live in the dry savannah. It has a large head with thick protective pads, or warts, on either side, an elongated snout with two pairs of tusks and a bristly mane. A warthog family consists of a female and her young. Male warthogs live alone or in small bachelor groups.

CREATURE PROFILE

Common name: Warthog

Scientific name: *Phacochoerus africanus*

Found in: Africa

Length: 1-1.5m (3-5 feet)

Weight: 50-150 kg (110-330 pounds)

Status: Least concern
There are plenty of warthogs in the wild

🐾 *Caracal*

🐾 *The tusks of a warthog are dangerous weapons*

VULTURE

Vultures are large birds of prey that feed on carcasses. It is because of this diet that these birds are known as scavengers. Although they are considered to be birds of prey, vultures rarely kill an animal on their own. Their feet are too weak and their claws too blunt to grasp live prey effectively.

Feeding on the dead

Vultures have many special features that are suited to their scavenging lifestyle. Their heads and sometimes even the necks lack feathers. This is a huge advantage, as vultures have to stick their heads into decaying carcasses Vultures also have excellent eyesight that helps them spot carcasses from a distance. Some vultures use their powerful beaks to rip the skin of the carcass.

Aided flight

Unlike most other flying birds, vultures have heavy bodies. They also have large, broad wings that help them lift their bodies into the air. However, most of the larger varieties rely on hot air to aid them in flight. Vultures are usually found in dry, open lands. Air close to the ground in these regions rises as it heats up, creating thermals. A thermal is a bubble of hot air. Vultures glide around inside the rising bubble, using the hot air to hold them up.

Cracking the shell

Vultures feed mainly on carcasses. However they do not hunt for food. Some of the larger species prey on young birds and small rodents. The palm-nut vulture feeds on oil-palm nuts and shellfish. Some vultures hunt in shallow waters for fish. The Egyptian vulture is known to crack open tough ostrich eggshells.

CREATURE PROFILE

Common name: Egyptian vulture

Scientific name: *Neophron percnopterus*

Found in: Africa, southern Europe, the Middle East and India

Length: 85 cm (2.8 feet)

Wingspan: 120 cm (4 feet)

Status: Low risk.

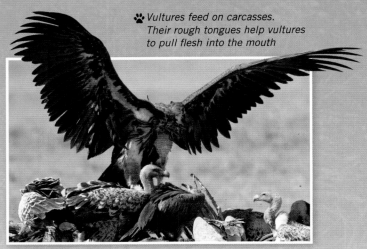

Vultures feed on carcasses. Their rough tongues help vultures to pull flesh into the mouth

Vultures often place their nests on the top branches of acacia trees

OSTRICH

The ostrich is a flightless bird. It is the largest bird in the world. It makes up for its inability to fly by running at a speed that can reach 65 km/hour (40 mph). In fact, the ostrich is the fastest creature on two legs.

Ostrich facts

The ostrich can grow up to an average height of eight feet and weighs between 90-135 kg (198-300 pounds). The adult male has mostly black feathers while the female and young male have greyish-brown feathers. The ostrich has strong legs. Each leg has two toes, one of which has a large claw. Like other birds, the ostrich does not have teeth, so it cannot chew its food. However, it compensates by swallowing small pebbles. These pebbles help grind the food inside the stomach and help in digestion.

Wings for all seasons

The wings of the ostrich might not help the bird fly, but they perform many other tasks. During mating displays, the male ostrich spreads its wings and engages in a peculiar courtship dance to impress the female. The wings are also used to provide shade to the eggs and, later on, the chicks. The soft feathers of the wings protect the bird from extreme weather conditions. In the summer, the bird fans itself with its wings. During the winter, it covers its bare legs with its wings to keep warm.

Safety measures

Ostriches have very long necks that help them detect danger from a long distance. Adult ostriches have very few enemies as they are aggressive and can deliver a fatal kick with their strong legs. Ostriches can also outrun most predators. However, the chicks often fall prey to predators such as jackals. The adult birds usually try to distract the predators with aggressive displays so that the chicks can escape during the confusion.

CREATURE PROFILE

Common name: Ostrich

Scientific name: *Struthio camelus*

Found in: Eastern and southern parts of Africa

Height: 2.1-2.7m (7-9 feet)

Weight: 90-135 kg (198-300 pounds)

Status: Threatened

The ostrich is the largest bird

The ostrich lacks teeth and so swallows pebbles to help grind the food in digestion

REPTILES OF THE SAVANNAHS

Apart from the great variety of mammals and birds, the African savannahs have some of the world's largest and most interesting reptiles. These include a wide range of monitor lizards, snakes and the gigantic Nile crocodile.

Monitor lizards

African savannahs are known for the large number monitor lizards that live there. Of these, the savannah monitor is the most well known. This huge lizard has a stout body with a thick skin. It is easily identified by the pimple like scales on the back of the neck. The savannah monitor's front legs have extremely sharp claws which are used for digging. It uses its longer rear legs for running. This lizard has a blue snake-like tongue. Its head can turn in all directions! Savannah monitors can expand their mouths like snakes, to swallow larger prey.

Snakes

The best-known snakes of the savannahs include the black mamba and the rock python. The black mamba is the largest venomous snake in Africa. It can grow up to 4.5m (14 feet) in length. It is also the world's fastest snake, known to reach speeds of about 20 km/hour (12 mph). Black mambas are ground-dwelling snakes and are found in open grasslands and rocky places. The rock python is the longest of all African snakes. It can reach a length of 6m (20 feet). The rock python is highly dependant on water and therefore hides in a deep burrow through the hottest parts of the summer.

Nile crocodile

The Nile crocodile is the largest of the three African crocodiles. An adult crocodile can grow up to 5m (16 feet) long. This crocodile has a long snout and is olive green in colour. Nile crocodiles live in freshwater swamps, rivers and lakes. These crocodiles are found only in the mainland of Africa and the island of Madagascar. Fish make up a major part of their diet. They also prey on bigger animals such as antelope, wild buffaloes and even big cats. Nile crocodiles also eat dead animals.

❧ The teeth of Nile crocodiles are conical and help grab and grip prey

CREATURE PROFILE

Common name: Nile crocodile

Scientific name: *Crocodylus niloticus*

Found in: Mainland Africa, Madagascar

Length: About 5m (16 feet)

Weight: About 450 kg (990 pounds)

Status: Least concern.

❧ The savannah monitor lizard is about 1-1.5m (3.3-5 feet) long

SAVANNAHS IN DANGER

The savannahs, and all the plants and animals living in it, are in grave danger of being wiped out. Human activities such as hunting, overgrazing and habitat destruction are the main threats to the survival of the savannahs.

Illegal hunting for tusks, horns and fur of animals are driving them to the brink of extinction

Climatic changes

Global warming is the effect of increase in the number of factories, and large scale deforestation. In the already hot savannah region, the rise in the average temperature is resulting in the death of many animals. The raised temperature is also destroying several species of grass and shrubs found there. Rainfall is becoming more scarce in the savannahs, which is making it difficult for plants and animals to survive.

Habitat destructions

Over the last few decades, the number of people living in the savannahs has risen. More and more land is being used up for housing and agriculture. Sometimes, they also cause fires that spread rapidly and destroy a large area of land. People also cut down the few trees that grow in the savannahs and use the wood to build houses and as fuel. This upsets the balance of nature.

Overgrazing

Domestic animals graze on the grass of the savannahs that is also the main diet of a large number of wild herbivores living there. This limits the food available to wild animals. Overgrazing forces many of the plant-eating animals such as the antelope to migrate in search of food. This unnatural migration often leads to their death. Wild animals also catch diseases from domestic animals.

Illegal hunting

Although strict laws have been introduced to protect wild animals, illegal hunting continues to threaten savannah wildlife. People hunt animals for their meat, skin and horns. This has led to a drastic decline in their populations. When there is a shortage of their prey in the wild, lions and leopards attack domestic animals. People living in the area then kill these wild animals. This is also a big reason for the dwindling number of savannah animals.